Holt
Mathematics

Course 2
Hands-On Lab Activities

HOLT, RINEHART AND WINSTON

A Harcourt Education Company

Austin • Orlando • Chicago • New York • Toronto • London • San Diego

ISBN 0-03-078319-4

1 2 3 4 5   170   09 08 07 06

Table of Contents

Holt Mathematics

Holt Mathematics

LESSON 1-2 **Hands-On Lab**
Working with Exponents

Use with Lesson 1-2

A base is multiplied by itself using as many factors as the number shown in the exponent. Two expressions with exponents can be multiplied or divided as long as the bases are the same.

$$\text{Base} \longrightarrow 5^3 = \underbrace{5 \cdot 5 \cdot 5}_{\text{expanded form}}$$

$$\overset{\text{exponent}}{\nearrow}$$

Activity 1

Work with a partner. Take turns rolling the number cube. The number that comes up on the first roll will be the base.

Roll the number cube a second time. This number will be the exponent for the first expression. Write the base and exponent together.

Roll the number cube a third time. This number will be the exponent for the second expression. Write the base and exponent together.

For example, if you roll a 6, a 5, and a 2, 6 is the base, 5 is the exponent for the first expression (6^5), and 2 is the exponent for the second expression (6^2).

Write the two expressions as a product.

$6^5 \times 6^2$

Next, write each expression in expanded form.

$(6 \times 6 \times 6 \times 6 \times 6) \times (6 \times 6)$

Write a new expression for the product using the same number as the base and the total number of factors as the exponent.

6^7

Take turns rolling the number cube and multiplying using other bases and exponents.

Hands-On Lab
Working with Exponents, *continued*

Activity 2

Roll the number cube three times as before and write two expressions with exponents that have the same base. This time, write the expression with the greater exponent as the numerator of a fraction and the other expression as the denominator. Next, write each expression in expanded form. Then simplify the fraction.

For example, Sandra rolls a 3, a 5, and a 2. So she writes

$$\frac{3^5}{3^2}$$

$$= \frac{3 \cdot 3 \cdot 3 \cdot 3 \cdot 3}{3 \cdot 3}$$

$$= 3 \cdot 3 \cdot 3 = 3^3$$

Take turns rolling the number cube and dividing using other bases and exponents.

Think and Discuss

1. How could you write an expression for the product $5^{100} \times 5^{20}$ with a single exponent?

_____

2. How could you write an expression for 5^{100} divided by 5^{20} with a single exponent?

_____

3. Why is it important that the base be the same?

_____

4. How could you write an expression for $(3^4)^2$ with a single exponent?

_____

Try This

Write an expression with a single exponent that is equal to each of the following.

1. $4^5 \times 4^3$ _____

2. $6^2 \times 6^3$ _____

3. $3^6 \times 3^2$ _____

4. $\dfrac{5^5}{5^2}$ _____

5. $\dfrac{2^8}{2^3}$ _____

6. $\dfrac{7^4}{7^3}$ _____

7. $(4^4)^3$ _____

8. $(2^4)^4$ _____

9. $(5^3)^2$ _____

Holt Mathematics

Hands-On Lab
Relative Error

Use with Lesson 1-4

Some quantities are difficult to measure exactly. These amounts must be measured as close as possible. The amount by which these measurements may be "off" is known as the *error*.

Activity

1. Officials in Kelso City estimate that approximately 152,000 ± 1000 people live in the city. The actual number is between a lower value of 152,000 − 1000 = 151,000 and an upper value of 152,000 + 1000 = 153,000. The error here is 1000 people.

   In Gilford, city officials estimate their city population to be 58,000 ± 1000.

   The size of the error is the same, 1000 people. You can also look at the ratio of each error to the total number of people. This ratio, written as a percent, is known as the *relative error*.

   $$\text{relative error} = \frac{\text{error}}{\text{total number}} \times 100$$

   For the Kelso City population, the relative error to the nearest tenth is
   $\frac{1000}{152,000} \approx 0.007 \times 100 = 0.7\%$.

	Population	Upper Value	Lower Value	Size of Error	Relative Error
Kelso City	152,000	153,000	151,000	± 1000	0.7%
Gilford	58,000			± 1000	
Lawrence	435,000			± 3000	

1. Complete the table for both Gilford's and Lawrence's population. Show your work.

3

Holt Mathematics

LESSON 1-4

Hands-On Lab
Relative Error, continued

Think and Discuss

1. The population of Gilford is smaller than the estimated population of Kelso City, but the relative error is larger. Why is this?

_____

_____

2. The error in the estimated Lawrence population is larger than that of Gilford, but the relative error is smaller. Why is this?

_____

_____

3. Why is the relative error approximately the same for Lawrence and Kelso City, even though the errors are different?

_____

_____

4. What can you conclude about the relationship between error and relative error?

_____

_____

5. What information does the relative error provide that the error alone does not give?

_____

_____

Try This

1. The population of Thomsen is estimated to be 25,300. Determine the relative error if the error is ±100.

_____

2. The population of Hillside is estimated to be 125,000. Find an error so that the relative error is smaller than that of Thomsen.

_____

3. Find an error so that the relative error is larger than that of Thomsen.

_____

Holt Mathematics

Hands-On Lab

LESSON 1-9 *Polynomials*

Use with Lesson 1-9

A term is any product, quotient, or power of numbers and variables. Algebraic expressions that contain one or more terms are called polynomials.

Polynomials with one term: $\frac{2}{3}$; $2g$; xy; $x/2$; a^3; $4x^2$

Polynomials with two terms: $x + 1$; $5a - b$; $xyz + 4$

Polynomials with three terms: $a + b + c$; $2x^2y - 5x^3 + 1$; $x + y - z$

Algebra tiles may be used to represent certain polynomials.

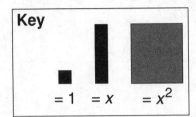

Key

$= 1$ $= x$ $= x^2$

Activity

You can simplify polynomials by regrouping and combining like terms. In the example below, a polynomial with 3 terms is written as an equivalent polynomial with 2 terms.

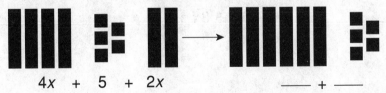

$3x + 2 + 4x$ $3x + 4x + 2$, or $7x + 2$

Use algebra tiles to simplify the polynomial $4x + 5 + 2x$.

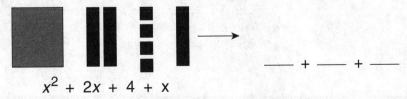

$4x + 5 + 2x$ ___ + ___

2. Use algebra tiles to simplify the expression below. Draw a picture of the tiles to represent the simplified polynomial.

$x^2 + 2x + 4 + x$ ___ + ___ + ___

Holt Mathematics

LESSON 1-9 Hands-On Lab
Polynomials, continued

Think and Discuss

1. Which arithmetic property did you use to reorder the algebra tiles?

_____

2. Explain how the polynomial $2x + 3x$ can be simplified using algebra tiles.

_____

_____

3. Without using algebra tiles, explain how the polynomial $2x + 3x$ can be written as an equivalent expression with one term.

_____

Try This

1. Draw a picture of the algebra tiles for the polynomial $3x + 4 + 2x$. Then simplify the polynomial and draw the algebra tiles for the simplified polynomial.

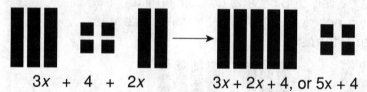

$3x + 4 + 2x$ $3x + 2x + 4$, or $5x + 4$

Simplify each polynomial.

2. $x^2 + x + 1 + 2x$ _____   3. $5x + 4 + x + 2$ _____

4. $x^2 + 3x + 6 + x + 1$ _____   5. $2x^2 + 3x + 1 + x + x^2$ _____

Holt Mathematics

Name _____ Date _____ Class _____

Hands-On Lab
Solving Equations with a Balance Scale

Use with Lesson 1-10

One way to think about equations is to think of a balance scale. Both sides must have the same value for the sides to balance and for the equation to be true. In this lab, a piece of paper will be divided in two to represent the two pans of a balance scale. Work with a partner to do this lab.

Left expression   Right expression

Activity 1

Draw a line down the middle of a piece of paper. Each side of the line stands for 1 of the pans of a balance scale.

Use play money to practice making equations using different combinations of quarters, dimes, nickels, and pennies. One person places one or more coins on one side of the line. The other partner matches the value using a different combination of coins. Below the coins, write the equation.

Notice how you can replace a coin or combination of coins with something that has the same value and the equation is still true. In the example below, the quarter has been replaced with 5 nickels. The equation is still true.

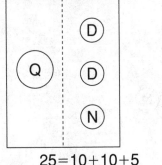 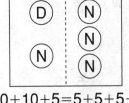

$$25 = 10 + 10 + 5 \qquad 10 + 10 + 5 = 5 + 5 + 5 +$$

Make and write 3 equations using the play money. Practice making substitutions of coins with the same value. Check that the equation is still true.

Holt Mathematics

LESSON 1-10 Hands-On Lab
Solving Equations with a Balance Scale, continued

Activity 2

You can add or subtract the same value from both sides of an equation without changing the balance of the scale.

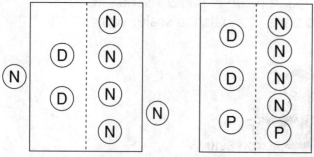

10+10 = 5+5+5+5   10+10+1 = 5+5+5+5+

Practice adding and subtracting the same amounts to both sides of your equations. Each time, write the new equation.

Activity 3

You can solve some equations by adding or subtracting the same quantity from each side. Use any object, such as a paper clip or eraser, to represent the unknown quantity, x.

Choose a number from 1 to 50. Write the number on a piece of paper, but don't show your partner. This number will be the unknown. Create an equation using some object to represent the unknown. Ask your partner to solve the equation. Check the solution.

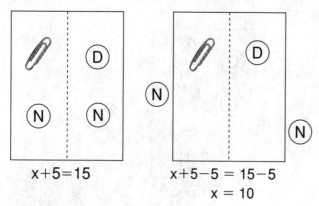

x+5=15   x+5−5 = 15−5
                   x = 10

Take turns writing and solving equations for at least 4 turns.

Holt Mathematics

Hands-On Lab

LESSON 1-10 *Solving Equation with a Balance scale, continued*

Think and Discuss

1. What would happen if you added different values to each side of an equation?

_____

_____

Try This

1. $a + 10 = 23$ _____

2. $9 = x + 3$ _____

3. $n + 4 = 6$ _____

4. $22 + 10 = k + 5 + 5$ _____

Holt Mathematics

LAB 1-11 **Hands-On Lab Recording Sheet (pp.50-51)**
Model Solving Equations

Activity

Think and Discuss

1. What operation did you use to solve the equation $3 + w = 11$ in **1**?

   What operation did you use to solve $3y = 15$ in **2**?

   _____

2. Compare using a balance scale and algebra tiles with using a mat and algebra tiles. Which method of modeling equations is more helpful to you? Explain.

   _____

   _____

   _____

Try This

Use a balance scale or algebra tiles to model and solve each equation.

1. $4x = 16$ **2.** $3 + 5 = n$ **3.** $5r = 15$

_____   _____   _____

4. $n + 7 = 12$ **5.** $y + 6 = 13$ **6.** $8 = 2r$

_____   _____   _____

7. $9 = 7 + w$ **8.** $18 = 6p$

_____   _____

Holt Mathematics

Hands-On Lab Recording Sheet

Model Integer Addition

Activity

Think and Discuss

1. Will $8 + (-3)$ and $-3 + 8$ give the same answer? Why or why not?

_____

_____

2. If you have more red chips than yellow chips in a group, is the sum of the chips positive or negative?

_____

_____

3. If you have more yellow chips than red chips in a group, is the sum of the chips positive or negative?

_____

_____

4. Make a rule for the sign of the answer when negative and positive integers are added. Give examples.

_____

_____

Try This

Use integer chips to find each sum.

1. $4 + (-7)$ **2.** $-5 + (-4)$ **3.** $-5 + 1$ **4.** $6 + (-4)$

_____   _____   _____   _____

Holt Mathematics

Hands-On Lab Recording Sheet
Model Integer Addition, continued

Write the addition problems modeled below.

5.

_____

6.

_____

7.

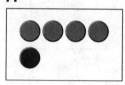

_____

8.

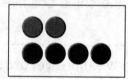

_____

Holt Mathematics

Hands-On Lab Recording Sheet (pp. 86-87)

LESSON 2-3 *Model Integer Subtraction*

Activity

Think and Discuss

1. How could you model the expression 0 − 5?

_____

_____

2. When you add zero pairs to model subtraction using chips, does it matter how many zero pairs you add?

_____

3. Would 2 − 3 have the same answer as 3 − 2? Why or why not?

_____

_____

_____

4. Make a rule for the sign of the answer when negative and positive integers are subtracted. Give examples.

_____

_____

_____

_____

_____

_____

_____

Try This

Use integer chips to find each sum.

1. 4 − 2 _____   **2.** −4 − (−2) _____   **3.** −2 − (−3) _____

Holt Mathematics

Hands-On Lab Recording Sheet (pp. 86-87)

LESSON 2-3 *Model Integer Subtraction, continued*

4. 3 − 4 _____   **5.** 2 − 3 _____   **6.** 0 − 3 _____

7. 5 − 3 _____   **8.** −3 − (−5) _____   **9.** 6 − (−4) _____

14   **Holt Mathematics**

Name _____ Date _____ Class _____

Activity 1

Think and Discuss

1. What is the sign of the product when you multiply two positive numbers? a negative and positive number? two negative numbers?

_____

2. If 12 were the answer to a multiplication problem, list all of the possible factors that are integers.

_____

Try This

Use integer chips to find each product.

1. $4 \cdot (-5)$ 2. $-3 \cdot 2$ 3. $1 \cdot (-6)$ 4. $-5 \cdot 2$

_____   _____   _____   _____

5. On days that Kathy has swimming lessons, she spends $2.00 of her allowance on snacks. Last week, Kathy had swimming lessons on Monday, Wednesday, and Friday. How much of her allowance did Kathy spend on snacks last week? Use integer chips to model the situation and solve the problem.

_____

Holt Mathematics

LESSON 2-4 Hands-On Lab Recording Sheet
Model Integer Multiplication and Division, continued

Activity 2

Think and Discuss

1. What is the sign of the answer when you divide two negative integers? a negative by a positive integer? a positive integer by a negative integer?

   _____

2. How are the multiplication and division of integers related?

   _____

Try This

Use integer chips to find each quotient.

1. $-21 \div 7$ 2. $-12 \div 4$ 3. $-8 \div 2$ 4. $-10 \div 5$

   _____   _____   _____   _____

5. Ty spent $18 of his allowance at the arcade. He hit baseballs, played pinball, and played video games. Each of these activities cost the same amount at the arcade. How much did each activity cost? Use integer chips to model the situation and solve the problem.

   _____

Holt Mathematics

Hands-On Lab Recording Sheet

LESSON 2-5 *Model Integer Equations*

Hands-On-Recording Sheet

Think and Discuss

1. When you remove tiles, what operation are you modeling?
When you add tiles, what operation are you modeling?

_____

_____

2. How can you use the original model to check your solution?

_____

3. To model $x - 6 = 2$, you must rewrite the equation as $x + (-6)$
$= 2$. Why are you allowed to do this?

_____

_____

Try This

Use algebra tiles to model and solve each equation.

1. $x + 7 = 10$ **2.** $x - 5 = -8$

_____   _____

3. $x + (-5) = -4$ **4.** $x - 2 = 1$

_____   _____

Holt Mathematics

LAB 2-5

Hands-On Lab Recording Sheet
Model Integer Equations, continued

5. $x + 4 = 8$

_____

6. $x + 3 = -2$

_____

7. $x + (-1) = 9$

_____

8. $x - 7 = -6$

_____

Holt Mathematics

LESSON 2-6

Hands-On Lab
Divisibility

Use with Lesson 2-6

Remember:
- A number is divisible by another number if there is no remainder when you divide.
- Even numbers end in 0, 2, 4, 6, or 8.
- Odd numbers end in 1, 3, 5, 7, or 9.

Activity

1. The following numbers are divisible by 2: **12; 248; 3,006;** and **420.**

   The following numbers are not divisible by 2: **81; 633; 5,977;** and **629.**

   Write a rule for numbers that are divisible by 2. Write two different numbers that are divisible by 2.

   _____

2. The following numbers are divisible by 3: **387; 426; 8,004;** and **420.**

   The following numbers are not divisible by 3: **782; 425; 1,451;** and **332.**

   Write a rule for numbers that are divisible by 3. (Hint: If you add a number's digits, what number is the sum divisible by?) Write two different numbers that are divisible by 3.

   _____

3. The following numbers are divisible by 5: **2,000; 425; 860;** and **9,015.**

   The following numbers are not divisible by 5: **3,046; 249; 551;** and **68.**

   Write a rule for numbers that are divisible by 5. Write two different numbers that are divisible by 5.

   _____

4. The following numbers are divisible by 8: **5,248; 16,320;** and **14,864.**

   The following numbers are not divisible by 8: **6,110; 14,596;** and **2,005.**

   Write a rule for numbers that are divisible by 8. Write two different numbers that are divisible by 8.

   _____

5. The following numbers are divisible by 9: **18; 378;** and **6,057.**

   The following numbers are not divisible by 9: **644; 5,817** and **6,524.**

   Write a rule for numbers that are divisible by 9. Write two differ ent numbers that are divisible by 9.

   _____

Holt Mathematics

Hands-On Lab

LAB 2-6 *Divisibility, continued*

Use with Lesson 2-6

The sieve of
Eratosthenes is a
method you can
use to find prime
numbers. Start
by crossing out
the number 1 in a
table like the one
at right. Next, circle

1	2	3	4	5	6	7	8	9	10
11	12	13	14	15	16	17	18	19	20
21	22	23	24	25	26	27	28	29	30
31	32	33	34	35	36	37	38	39	40
41	42	43	44	45	46	47	48	49	50
51	52	53	54	55	56	57	58	59	60
61	62	63	64	65	66	67	68	69	70
71	72	73	74	75	76	77	78	79	80
81	82	83	84	85	86	87	88	89	90
91	92	93	94	95	96	97	98	99	100

the number 2, and then cross out all of the numbers that are
divisible by 2. next, circle the number 3, and then cross out all of the
numbers that are divisible by 3. Continue in this pattern until all of
the composite numbers are crossed out and all of the prime
numbers are circled. Use this method to find all of the prime
numbers in the table.

Think and Discuss

1. Are all even numbers divisible by 2? Why or why not?

_____

_____

2. Are all odd numbers divisible by 3? Why or why not?

_____

_____

Holt Mathematics

Hands-On Lab

LAB 2-6 *Divisibility, continued*

Try This

For each divisibility rule, name one number that would satisfy the rule and one that would not.

	A number is divisible by...	Divisible	Not Divisible
1.	2 if the digit is even (0, 2, 4, 6, or 8).		
2.	3 if the sum of the digits is divisible by 3.		
3.	4 if the last two digits form a number divisible by 4.		
4.	5 if the last digit is 0 or 5.		
5.	6 if the last three digits from a number divisible by 8.		
6.	8 if the last three digits is divisible by 9.		
7.	9 if the sum of the digits is divisible by 9.		
8.	10 if the digit is 0.		

Use number tiles to find a number in which no digit is repeated for each description.

9. 4-digit number divisible by 5 and 10

_____

10. 4-digit number divisible by 3 and 5

_____

11. 4-digit number divisible by 3, 5, and 9

_____

12. 4-digit number divisible by 4 and 9

_____

13. 4-digit number divisible by 3 and 4

_____

14. 3-digit number divisible by 2, 3, and 6

_____

Holt Mathematics

Hands-On Lab
Absolute Value of Rational and Real Numbers

Think and Discuss

The absolute value of a rational number, such as $\frac{6}{5}$, 0.85, or −0.33..., is the distance between the number and zero on the number line. For example, the numbers 4.5 and −4.5 are both 4.5 units from 0 on the number line. Just as with integers, a rational number and its opposite have the same absolute value since both are the same distance from 0.

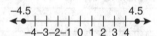

The absolute value of 4.5 is written |4.5|; the absolute value of −4.5 is written |−4.5|. Both equal 4.5.

Every rational number can be written as a decimal that either comes to an end, such as 0.1254, or repeats, such as 0.11... Decimal numbers that do not end or repeat are known as *irrational numbers*. Example of irrational numbers include π and $\sqrt{2}$. But just like integers and rational numbers, the absolute value of an irrational number is also its distance from zero. For example, |π| = π and |−π| = π. Both π and −π, or approximately 3.14 and −3.14, can be shown to be the same distance from 0 on the number line.

Activity

1. On the number line, label the point or points that are a distance of 6.25 units from 0.

```
←┼┼┼┼┼┼┼┼┼┼┼┼┼┼┼┼┼┼┼→
 −9−8−7−6−5−4−3−2−1 0 1 2 3 4 5 6 7 8 9
```

2. On the number line above, label the points or point with an absolute value of π. (Use 3.14 for π.)

3. On the above number line, mark and label the point that has the same absolute value as $-\frac{3}{2}$.

4. What are the two possible solutions for |x| ÷ 14.8?

_____

Holt Mathematics

LESSON 2-11 Hands-On Lab
Absolute Value of Rational and Real Numbers, *continued*

Think and Discuss

1. Why is the absolute value of a number either positive or zero?

   _____

   _____

2. True or False: The absolute value of a number is equal to the absolute value of its opposite. Explain your answer and give an example.

   _____

   _____

   _____

   _____

3. Why does the equation $|x| = 14.8$ have two solutions?

   _____

   _____

Try This

Simplify.

1. $|10.01|$

2. $|-7.14|$

3. $|-\sqrt{2}|$

4. $|-3| + |3|$

5. $|-5.2| + |3.41|$

6. $\left|-\dfrac{3}{8}\right| + \left|\dfrac{3}{8}\right|$

Write two solutions for each equation.

7. $|a| = 2$

8. $|b| = \sqrt{5}$

9. $|c| = 6\dfrac{7}{12}$

10. Solve the riddle.

    I am an integer that is less than 22.835.

    My absolute value is more than π.

    I am less than 5 units from 0 on the number line.

    Who am I?

    _____

Holt Mathematics

LAB 3-3 **Hands-On Lab Recording Sheet (pp. 158–159)**
Model Decimal Multiplication

Activity 1

1. Use base-ten blocks to model each expression.

a. 2 • 0.001 _____

b. 0.11 • 3 _____

c. 5 • 0.1 _____

d. 1.1 • 4 _____

2. Use base-ten blocks to model each expression.

a. 5 • 0.2 _____

b. 8 • 0.11 _____

c. 7 • 0.15 _____

d. 6 • 0.12 _____

Think and Discuss

1. Why can't you use base-ten blocks to model multiplying a decimal by a decimal?

_____

Holt Mathematics

Hands-On Lab Recording Sheet (pp. 158–159)

LAB 3-3 *Model Decimal Multiplication, continued*

Try This

Use base-ten blocks to model each expression.

1. 4 • 0.5 _____

Show your work.

2. 2 • 0.04 _____

Show your work.

3. 3 • 0.16 _____

Show your work.

4. 5 • 0.123 _____

Show your work.

5. 6 • 0.2 _____

Show your work.

6. 3 • 0.33 _____

Show your work.

7. 0.25 • 5 _____

Show your work.

8. 0.42 • 3 _____

Show your work.

Holt Mathematics

Hands-On Lab Recording Sheet (pp. 158–159)
Model Decimal Multiplication, continued

Activity 2

1. Use decimal grids to model each expression.

a. 0.3 • 0.4

b. 0.1 • 0.1

_____

_____

c. 0.2 • 0.2

d. 0.1 • 0.2

_____

_____

Think and Discuss

1. Explain the steps you would take to model 0.5 • 0.5 with a decimal grid.

_____

_____

2. How could you use decimal grids to model multiplying a decimal by a whole number?

_____

_____

Try This

Use a decimal grid to model each expression.

1. 0.6 • 0.6

2. 0.5 • 0.4

_____

_____

Holt Mathematics

Name _____ Date _____ Class _____

3. 0.3 • 0.8 _____

4. 0.2 • 0.8 _____

5. 3 • 0.3 _____

6. 0.8 • 0.8 _____

7. 2 • 0.5 _____

8. 0.1 • 0.9 _____

Holt Mathematics

LESSON 3-4 Hands-On Lab Recording Sheet (pp. 164–165)
Model Decimal Division

Activity

Think and Discuss

1. Explain why you think division is or is not commutative.

   _____

   _____

   _____

   _____

2. What type of data would you want to display using a circle graph?

   _____

   _____

   _____

   _____

Holt Mathematics

Hands-On Lab Recording Sheet (pp. 164–165)

LESSON 3-4 *Model Decimal Division, continued*

Try This

Use decimal grids to find each quotient.

1. 0.8 ÷ 4

2. 0.6 ÷ 4

3. 0.9 ÷ 0.3

4. 0.6 ÷ 0.4

_____

_____

_____

_____

5. 4.5 ÷ 9

6. 1.35 ÷ 3

7. 3.6 ÷ 1.2

8. 4.2 ÷ 2.1

i_____

_____

_____

_____

Holt Mathematics

Hands-On Lab Recording Sheet (pp. 184–185)

LAB 3-8 *Model Fraction Addition and Subtraction*

Activity

1. Use fraction bars to evaluate each expression.

   a. $\frac{1}{3} + \frac{1}{3}$ _____

   b. $\frac{2}{4} + \frac{1}{4}$ _____

   c. $\frac{3}{12} + \frac{2}{12}$ _____

   d. $\frac{1}{5} + \frac{2}{5}$ _____

2. Use fraction bars to evaluate each expression.

   a. $\frac{1}{2} + \frac{1}{3}$ _____

   b. $\frac{1}{2} + \frac{1}{4}$ _____

   c. $\frac{1}{3} + \frac{1}{6}$ _____

   d. $\frac{1}{4} + \frac{1}{6}$ _____

3. Use fraction bars to evaluate each expression.

   a. $\frac{3}{4} + \frac{3}{4}$ _____

   b. $\frac{2}{3} + \frac{1}{2}$ _____

   c. $\frac{5}{6} + \frac{1}{4}$ _____

   d. $\frac{3}{8} + \frac{3}{4}$ _____

4. Use fraction bars to evaluate each expression.

   a. $\frac{2}{3} - \frac{1}{3}$ _____

   b. $\frac{1}{4} - \frac{1}{6}$ _____

   c. $\frac{1}{2} - \frac{1}{3}$ _____

   d. $\frac{3}{4} - \frac{2}{3}$ _____

Holt Mathematics

Hands-On Lab Recording Sheet (pp. 184–185)

LAB 3-8 *Model Fraction Addition and Subtraction, continued*

Think and Discuss

1. Model and solve $\frac{3}{4} - \frac{1}{6}$. Explain your steps.

   Show your work.

   _____

   _____

   _____

2. Two students solved $\frac{1}{4} + \frac{1}{3}$ in different ways. One got $\frac{7}{12}$ for the answer and the other got $\frac{2}{7}$. Use models to show which student is correct.

   Show your work.

3. Find three different ways to model $\frac{1}{2} + \frac{1}{4}$.

   Show your work.

Holt Mathematics

Hands-On Lab Recording Sheet (pp. 184–185)

LAB 3-8 *Model Fraction Addition and Subtraction, continued*

Try This

Use fraction bars to model each expression.

1. $\frac{1}{2} + \frac{1}{2}$ _____

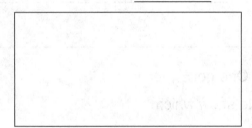

2. $\frac{2}{3} + \frac{1}{6}$ _____

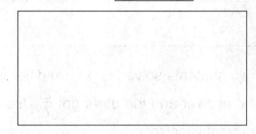

3. $\frac{1}{4} + \frac{1}{6}$ _____

4. $\frac{1}{3} + \frac{7}{12}$ _____

5. $\frac{5}{12} - \frac{1}{3}$ _____

6. $\frac{1}{2} - \frac{1}{4}$ _____

7. $\frac{3}{4} - \frac{1}{6}$ _____

8. $\frac{2}{3} - \frac{1}{4}$ _____

Holt Mathematics

Hands-On Lab Recording Sheet (pp. 184–185)

LAB 3-8 *Model Fraction Addition and Subtraction, continued*

9. You ate $\frac{1}{4}$ of a pizza for lunch and $\frac{5}{8}$ of the pizza for dinner. How much of the pizza did you eat in all?

_____

10. It is $\frac{5}{6}$ mile from your home to the library. After walking $\frac{3}{4}$ mile, you stop to visit a friend on your way to the library. How much farther do you have left to walk to reach the library?

_____

Holt Mathematics

Hands-On Lab Recording Sheet (pp. 194–195)

LESSON 3-10 *Model Fraction Multiplication and Division*

Activity 1

Think and Discuss

1. Are $\frac{2}{3} \cdot \frac{1}{5}$ and $\frac{1}{5} \cdot \frac{2}{3}$ modeled the same way? Explain.

_____

_____

_____

_____

2. When you multiply a positive fraction by a positive fraction, the product is less than either factor. Why?

_____

_____

_____

_____

Try This

Use a grid to find each product.

1. $\frac{1}{2} \cdot \frac{1}{2}$ 2. $\frac{3}{4} \cdot \frac{2}{3}$ 3. $\frac{5}{8} \cdot \frac{1}{3}$ 4. $\frac{2}{5} \cdot \frac{5}{6}$

_____   _____   _____   _____

Holt Mathematics

Name _____ Date _____ Class _____

Activity 2

1. Are $\frac{3}{4} \div \frac{1}{6}$ and $\frac{1}{6} \div \frac{3}{4}$ modeled the same way? Explain.

_____

_____

_____

2. When you divide fractions, is the quotient greater than or less than the dividend and the divisor? Explain?

_____

_____

_____

Try This

Use a grids to find each quotient.

1. $\frac{7}{12} \div \frac{1}{6}$ **2.** $\frac{4}{5} \div \frac{3}{10}$ **3.** $\frac{2}{3} \div \frac{4}{9}$ **4.** $3\frac{2}{5} \div \frac{3}{5}$

_____   _____   _____   _____

Holt Mathematics

Hands-On Lab
Model Fraction Multiplication and Division

Use with Lesson 3-10

KEY	REMEMBER:
 = 1	• The multiplication sign can mean "of."

You can use pattern blocks to model multiplying and dividing fractions.

Activity

1. Determine the fraction that each shape represents . Draw a sketch to explain your answer .

   a.

   b.

   c.

   d.

   e.

   You can use pattern blocks to model multiplying a fraction by a whole number.

   To evaluate $\frac{1}{12} \cdot 5$, arrange pattern blocks as shown.

2. Use pattern blocks to evaluate each expression .

   a. $\frac{1}{2} \cdot 2$

   b. $\frac{1}{6} \cdot 2$

   c. $\frac{1}{3} \cdot 2$

   d. $\frac{2}{12} \cdot 3$

   When you multiply two fractions that are less than 1, the product will always be less than either fraction.

   To evaluate $\frac{1}{8} \cdot \frac{2}{3}$, arrange pattern blocks as shown.

   Show $\frac{2}{3}$. Find which shape uses 8 blocks to exactly cover $\frac{2}{3}$.

   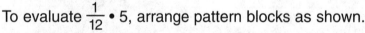
   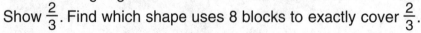

   $\frac{1}{8}$ of $\frac{2}{3}$ is $\frac{1}{12}$. $\frac{1}{8} \cdot \frac{2}{3} = \frac{1}{12}$

Holt Mathematics

Name _____ Date _____ Class _____

Hands-On-Lab
LESSON
3-10 *Model Fraction Multiplication and Division, continued*

3. Use pattern blocks to evaluate each expression.

a. $\frac{1}{4} \cdot \frac{1}{3}$ **b.** $\frac{1}{2} \cdot \frac{2}{3}$

c. $\frac{1}{3} \cdot \frac{1}{2}$ **d.** $\frac{5}{6} \cdot \frac{1}{2}$

You can use pattern blocks to model dividing fractions.

To evaluate $.\frac{1}{2} \div \frac{1}{4}$, arrange pattern blocks as shown.

Show $\frac{1}{2}$. Find the number of $\frac{1}{4}$'s that cover $\frac{1}{2}$ exactly.

4. Use pattern blocks to evaluate each expression.

a. $\frac{1}{3} \div \frac{1}{6}$ **b.** $\frac{1}{2} \div \frac{1}{12}$

c. $1 \div \frac{1}{4}$ **d.** $\frac{1}{2} \div \frac{1}{4}$

Think and Discuss

1. Are $\frac{1}{4} \cdot \frac{1}{3}$ and $\frac{1}{3} \cdot \frac{1}{4}$ modeled the same way? Explain.

_____

2. If you used 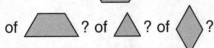 to model one whole, what would be the value

of _____? of _____? of _____?

_____

3. Use pattern blocks to order the fractions from least to greatest.

$\frac{1}{3}$ $\frac{1}{6}$ $\frac{1}{4}$ $\frac{1}{2}$ $\frac{1}{12}$ _____

What do you notice? _____

Holt Mathematics

Hands-On Lab

Model Fraction Multiplication and Division, continued

Try This

Model each expression with pattern blocks using 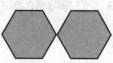 as one whole.

1. $\frac{3}{4} \cdot 1$

2. $\frac{1}{2} \cdot \frac{1}{6}$

3. $\frac{1}{2} \div \frac{1}{2}$

4. $\frac{2}{3} \cdot \frac{3}{6}$

5. $\frac{3}{4} \cdot \frac{1}{3}$

6. $2 \div \frac{1}{4}$

7. $\frac{1}{4} \cdot \frac{2}{3}$

8. $\frac{2}{3} \div \frac{1}{6}$

9. It took $\frac{1}{2}$ hour for your sister to drive to your aunt's house. If she was in traffic for $\frac{1}{3}$ of that time, how long was she in traffic? _____

LESSON 3-11

Hands-On Lab

Multiplying and Dividing Rational Numbers

Use with Lesson 3-11

You can use the rules for exponents to multiply, divide, and simplify rational numbers.

Rules for Exponents

To multiply two numbers with the same base, keep the base and add the exponents.
To divide a number by a number with the same base, keep the base and subtract the exponent of the second number from the exponent of the first.
To raise a power to a power, keep the base and multiply the exponents.

$$2^3 \cdot 2^5 = 2^8 \qquad\qquad \frac{3^6}{3^2} = 3^4 \qquad\qquad (5^2)^3 = 5^6$$

Activity

One way to simplify the rational number $\frac{32}{48}$ is to start by writing each

number as the product of prime factors. Recall that a prime number
is a number whose only factors are itself and 1.

$$\frac{32}{48} = \frac{2 \cdot 2 \cdot 2 \cdot 2 \cdot 2}{2 \cdot 2 \cdot 2 \cdot 2 \cdot 3}$$

Notice that you could also write this as $\frac{32}{48} = \frac{2}{2} \cdot \frac{2}{2} \cdot \frac{2}{2} \cdot \frac{2}{2} \cdot \frac{2}{3}$. Because

the value of $\frac{2}{2}$ is 1, the rational number $\frac{32}{48}$ is equal to

$1 \cdot 1 \cdot 1 \cdot 1 \cdot \frac{2}{3}$, or $\frac{2}{3}$. Therefore, $\frac{32}{48} = \frac{2}{3}$.

A shorthand way of writing this is with exponents.

$$\frac{32}{48} = \frac{2^5}{2^4 \cdot 3}$$
$$= \frac{2^{5-4}}{3}$$
$$= \frac{2}{3}$$

You can also use exponents when you multiply and divide rational numbers.
First, write each number as the product of expressions with exponents and
bases prime-number. Then combine expressions with the same base by adding
and subtracting their exponents according to the rules given above.

$$\frac{9}{16} \cdot \frac{24}{5} = \frac{3^2}{2^4} \cdot \frac{2^3 \cdot 3}{5}$$
$$= \frac{3^2 \cdot 2^3 \cdot 3}{2^4 \cdot 5}$$
$$= \frac{3^{2+1}}{2^{4-3} \cdot 5}$$
$$= \frac{3^3}{2^1 \cdot 5}$$
$$= \frac{27}{10}, \text{ or } 2\frac{7}{10}$$

Holt Mathematics

Hands-On Lab

LESSON 3-11 *Multiplying and Dividing Rational Numbers, continued*

Think and Discuss

1. How can you use exponents to divide rational numbers?

_____

_____

_____

2. Explain why $\frac{2^3}{2^4}$ is $\frac{1}{2}$, and not $\frac{2}{1}$.

_____

_____

_____

Try This

Write each number as the product of prime factors. Then use the rules for exponents to simplify.

1. $\frac{8}{12}$ _____

2. $\frac{24}{16}$ _____

3. $\frac{44}{18}$ _____

4. $\frac{36}{225}$ _____

5. $\frac{54}{25} \cdot \frac{125}{9}$ _____

6. $\frac{9}{10} \cdot \frac{25}{27}$ _____

7. $\frac{8}{9} \cdot \frac{21}{12}$ _____

8. $\frac{56}{81} \cdot \frac{18}{8}$ _____

9. $\frac{3}{4} \div \frac{9}{2}$ _____

10. $\frac{4}{5} \div \frac{16}{25}$ _____

11. $\frac{27}{32} \div \frac{9}{10}$ _____

12. $\frac{25}{36} \div \frac{5}{9}$ _____

13. $1\frac{1}{2} \cdot \frac{4}{9}$ _____

14. $1\frac{1}{4} \cdot 1\frac{3}{5}$ _____

15. $2\frac{1}{2} \div 1\frac{1}{10}$ _____

16. $3\frac{1}{3} \div 1\frac{1}{9}$ _____

Holt Mathematics

Hands-On Lab

LESSON 4-3

Input/Output Tables

Use with Lesson 4-3

A function is a rule that matches one member of one set to exactly one member of another set.

Activity

Many real processes, such as the distance a ship travels, the amount a stock is worth, or the daily temperature, generate number pairs that can be represented in data tables. If the entry in one column matches exactly one value in the second column, the table represents a function. Tables such as these are sometimes known as input/output tables. In this activity, you will drop a ball from various heights and measure how high the ball bounces. Use any ball that is available, such as a "super" ball, a golf ball, or a tennis ball. Drop the ball from the heights shown in the table and use a meter stick to measure the bounce height.

Drop height	200 cm	150 cm	100 cm	75 cm	50 cm
Bounce height					

1. For a given drop height, such as 100 cm, are there several different bounce heights or only one bounce height?

   _____

2. Divide each value of bounce height by the corresponding value of drop height. Are these values about the same?

   _____

Drop height	200 cm	150 cm	100 cm	75 cm	50 cm
Bounce height					
Bounce height / Drop height					

3. Suppose the fraction $\dfrac{\text{Bounce height}}{\text{Drop height}}$ is equal to 0.8. Then the rule that describes the relation between bounce height and drop height can be written as bounce height = 0.8 × (drop height) or in symbols as $b = 0.8 \times d$. Write an equation that described the rule for your table.

_____

Holt Mathematics

LESSON 4-3

Hands-On Lab
Input/Output Tables, continued

Think and Discuss

1. If a car is moving at 55 km/h, the distance it travels can be expressed by the function $d = 55t$. Complete a table showing the distance a car would travel each hour.

Time (t)	1	2	3	4	5
$d = 55t$	55				

2. A teacher decides to "curve" the grades on an exam using the formula new grade $= 10\sqrt{\text{old grade}}$. Complete the input/output table for this equation.

Old grade		36	49	64	81	100
New grade $= 10\sqrt{\text{old grade}}$						

Try This

Answer the following questions.

1. A racecar is moving at 17.0 m/s. How far will it travel in 15 s?

_____

2. Write a function that will give the distance the racecar in problem 1 will travel in t seconds.

_____

3. Examine the following tables and decide whether the data are related by a function in each case

a.

1	2	3	4	5
1	4	9	16	25

_____

b.

x	5	6	5	7	8
y	3	4	2	13	11

_____

c.

x	5	6	7	8	9
y	0	0	0	0	0

_____

Holt Mathematics

Name _____ Date _____ Class _____

Hands-On Lab
Functions and Variables

Use with Lesson 4-4

A graph of a function shows how a change in one quantity causes
another quantity to change as well. As the input variable (*x*) is
changed, the output variable (*y*) also changes.

Activity

In the equation $y = 3x + 4$, how does *y* change each time *x* is
increased by 1?

Replace variable *x* in the equation with the first value for *x* in the
table. Simplify to find the corresponding value for *y*. Write the value
for *y* in the table.

$y = 3x + 4$

$y = 3(1) + 4$

$y = 3 + 4$

$y = 7$

Now do the same to find the values for *y* that correspond to the
other values for *x* and write those in the table.

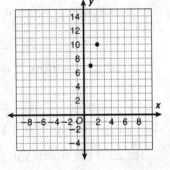

$y = 3x + 4$			
x	1	2	3
y	7		

On the graph, plot the third point from the table and connect
the dots with a line.

As the value for *x* increases by 1, how does the value for
y change?

_____

_____

Holt Mathematics

LESSON 4-4   # Hands-On Lab
Functions and Variables, continued

Think and Discuss

1. Describe how each change in x would affect the value for y in the function $y = 3x + 4$.

   a. An increase of 100

   _____

   b. A decrease of 50

   _____

2. In the function $y = 3x + 4$, what change in x would cause a decrease of 60 in y?

   _____

   _____

Try This

1. Your watch loses 5 minutes every day as the battery dies.

   a. Write a rule that shows how many minutes it will lose each day using the variable x for the number of days.

   _____

   b. Describe how the time on the watch changes over a period of a week.

   _____

2. Graph the function $y = x - 4$.

   a. Plot ordered pairs when the values of x are 2, 1, 0, −1, −2.

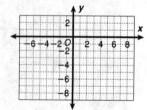

   b. How does the value of y change when x increases by 4?

   _____

3. In the function $y = 2x$, how does the value of y change when x is doubled?

   _____

Holt Mathematics

Hands-On Lab Recording Sheet (pp. 246–247)

LESSON 4-6 *Explore Linear Functions*

Activity

Think and Discuss

1. How can you tell by looking at a function table whether the graph of the function is a line?

_____

_____

2. Is $y = x^2$ a linear function? Explain your answer.

_____

_____

_____

Holt Mathematics

LESSON 4-6 Hands-On Lab Recording Sheet (pp. 246–247)
Explore Linear Functions, continued

Try This

1. Use square tiles to model each pattern.

2. Model the next two sets in each pattern using square tiles.

3. Complete each table.

4. Graph the ordered pairs in each table, and then tell whether the function is linear.

Pattern 1

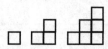

Number of Tiles	Perimeter
	4
	8
	12

Pattern 2

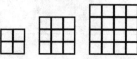

Perimeter	Area
8	
12	
16	

Pattern 3

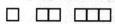

Perimeter	Area
4	
6	
8	

Holt Mathematics

Name _____ Date _____ Class _____

Hands-On Lab
Linear and Nonlinear Functions

Activity

Sarah goes for a hike on afternoon. The table shows the number of miles she has walked as time passes. Sarah then drew a graph to represent this data.

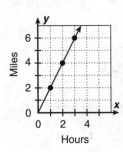

x (hours)	y (miles)
0	0
1	2
2	4
3	6

1. Write the equation that represents this relationship.

_____

2. What type of relationship does this represent?

_____

Notice that as *x* increases by a constant value, such as 1, *y* increases by a constant value, such as 2 in this example. The ratio of each *y*-value to its *x*-value is a constant ratio:

On her hike, Sarah walks through a rectangular-shaped forest that has an area of 24 square acres. After returning from her walk she makes a table listing some of the dimensions this forest could have. For example, if the length, *x*, of the forest is 2 acres, the width, *y*, is $24 \div 2 = 12$ acres since width = area ÷ length.

x (hours)	y (miles)
1	24
2	12
3	8
4	
6	
8	
12	
24	

3. Complete the table of values.

4. What is the relationship between each *x*- and *y*-value? _____

The equation for this function is $y = 20 \div x$ or $y = \dfrac{20}{x}$.

Sarah draws part of its graph:

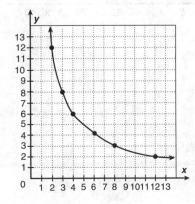

Holt Mathematics

LESSON 4-ext **Hands-On Lab**
Linear and Nonlinear Functions

Think and Discuss

1. Is the function $y = \dfrac{20}{x}$ a linear function? Why or why not?

_____

2. Find the corresponding y-value for $x = \dfrac{1}{2}$ and $x = 96$.

_____

3. Can x or y ever equal 0? Explain by setting x, then y, equal to 0.

_____

_____

Try This

You want to make a rectangular garden with an area of 20 square feet.

1. Complete the table of length, x, and width, y, values for this garden. _____

2. Graph these values on graph paper.

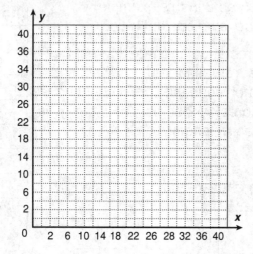

x (hours)	y (miles)
$\dfrac{1}{4}$	
$\dfrac{1}{2}$	
1	
2	
4	
5	
10	
20	
40	$\dfrac{1}{2}$
80	$\dfrac{1}{4}$

Holt Mathematics

Hands-On Lab

LESSON
5-3 *Identifying and Writing Proportions*

Use with Lesson 5-3

The best way to understand the possibilities of proportion is to experiment. Once you have identified a proportion you can manipulate the numbers to increase, decrease or change the proportion. As long as you increase or decrease each side of the proportion by an equal number, you keep the same basic proportion. If you increase or decrease each side by a different number, you have changed the basic proportion.

Activity

Color a looseleaf sheet of lined paper with markers. For example, color the top half purple and the bottom half green. Then use scissors to make ribbons by cutting along the lines. Make two purple strips and three green strips. Write the proportion of purple to green in three different ways.

2 to 3   2:3 $\frac{2}{3}$

Measure and cut each strip into three equal pieces. Write the new proportion.

6 to 9   6:9 $\frac{6}{9}$

Now cut each purple piece in half, and each green strip into thirds. Write the new proportion.

12 to 27   12:27 $\frac{12}{27}$

Notice that 6:9 can be reduced to the basic proportion, 2:3, by dividing each number by 3. But when you divide 12:27 by 3, the result is 4:9. This is because the purple and green pieces were cut into different lengths. To retain the basic proportion, each color must be multiplied or divided by the same factor.

So, if you had cut the six purple and nine green pieces into halves, you would have retained the basic proportion of 2:3.

6:9 = 12:18 = 2:3

Holt Mathematics

LESSON **Hands-On Lab**

5-3 *Identifying and Writing Proportions, continued*

Think and Discuss

1. Suppose you cut each of the 12 purple pieces into 3 equal pieces, and the 27 green strips into 2 equal pieces. What is the new proportion? How does this new proportion relate to the original proportion of 2:3?

_____

_____

_____

_____

Try This

1. Use colored paper to make strips in a proportion of 1:4. Then cut each strip into an equal number of pieces. Write your new proportion, then cut one color into 3 pieces and the other color into 4 pieces. Can you think of an easy way to make the final proportion equal to 1:4?

_____

_____

_____

_____

Holt Mathematics

Hands-On Lab Recording Sheet (p. 291)

LESSON 5-6

Generate Formulas to Convert Units

Activity

Think and Discuss

1. Make a conjecture about the relationship between picas and inches.

   _____

2. Use your conjecture to write a formula relating inches *n* to picas *p*.

   _____

3. How many picas wide is a sheet of paper that is $8\frac{1}{2}$ in. wide?

   _____

Try This

Using inches for x-coordinates and picas for y-coordinates, write ordered pairs for the data in the table. Then plot the points and draw a graph.

1. What shape is the graph?

   _____

2. Use the graph to find the number of picas that is equal to 6 inches.

   _____

3. Use the graph to find the number of inches that is equal to 18 picas.

   _____

4. A designer is laying out a page in a magazine. The dimensions of a photo are 18 picas by 15 picas. She doubles the dimensions of the photo. What are the new dimensions of the photo in inches?

   _____

Holt Mathematics

LESSON 5-7 Hands-On Lab Recording Sheet (pp 298–299)
Make Similar Figures

Think and Discuss

1. Sarah wants to increase the size of her rectangular backyard patio. Why must she change both dimensions of the patio to create a patio similar to the original?

   _____

   _____

2. In a backyard, a plot of land that is 5 yd × 8 yd is used to grow tomatoes. The homeowner wants to decrease this plot to 4 yd × 6 yd. Will the new plot be similar to the original? Why or why not?

   _____

   _____

   _____

Try This

1. A rectangle is 3 feet long and 7 feet wide. What is the width of a similar rectangle whose length is 9 feet?

   _____

2. A rectangle is 6 feet long and 12 feet wide. What is the length of a similar rectangle whose width is 4 feet?

   _____

Holt Mathematics

Hands-On Lab Recording Sheet (pp 298–299)

LESSON 5-7 *Make Similar Figures, continued*

Use square tiles to model similar rectangles to solve each proportion.

3. _____   4. _____

5. _____   6. _____

7. _____   8. _____

9. _____   10. _____

Holt Mathematics

LESSON 5-7 Hands-On Lab
Using Similar Figures and Proportions

Use with Lesson 5-7

Working in groups with graph paper you can explore similar figures. This activity challenges you to recognize similarity and to use the concept to change similar figures.

Activity

Working in groups, you will draw a figure, two similar figures, and one dissimilar figure. Then you will cut out your figures, combine them with those drawn by other groups and try to identify which figures are similar and dissimilar.

Using graph paper, draw a right triangle—make the vertical leg 12 squares, the horizontal leg 16 squares, and then connect the endpoints to make the hypotenuse.

Then draw two similar triangles. For example *Triangle A* would have a vertical leg of 24 squares and a horizontal leg of 32 squares; *Triangle B* would have a vertical leg of 6 squares and a horizontal leg of 8 squares. In other words, *Triangle A* is twice as large as the original, and *Triangle B* is half as large.

Then draw a dissimilar triangle. For example, *Triangle C* would have a vertical leg of 10 squares and a horizontal leg of 12 squares.

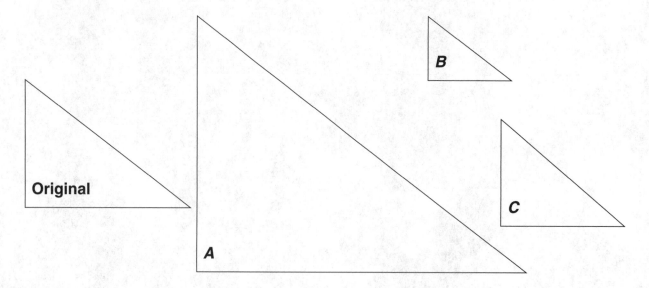

Holt Mathematics

Hands-On Lab

LESSON 5-7
Using Similar Figures and Proportions, *continued*

Cut out all 4 of your triangles, including the original. Mix your cutouts in a box with those made by other groups. Then have a member of each group draw 4 triangles at random from the box.

Each group should measure, compare the dimensions of its 4 triangles, and identify which triangles are congruent, which are similar, and which are dissimilar to the original. When all the dissimilar triangles have been identified, compare them to see if any of these are similar to one another.

Think and Discuss

1. How can you make the dissimilar *Triangle C* similar to the original?

_____

_____

_____

_____

_____

2. Why would this activity be unsuccessful using circles?

_____

_____

_____

Try This

1. Perform the activity above with other figures, such as parallelograms, trapezoids, and hexagons. Are some figures easier to make similar than others? Why?

_____

_____

_____

_____

Holt Mathematics

Hands-On Lab
5-7A Areas of Similar Figure

LESSON

Use with Lesson 5-7

In this activity you will explore how the areas of similar figures are related.

Activity

1. Use square tiles or grid paper to make two similar rectangles like the ones shown below. Each tile or square on the paper has an area of one square unit. Below each rectangle, write the area of the rectangle.

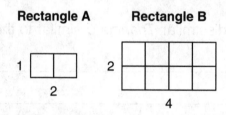

Rectangle A   Rectangle B

Area = _____ square units   Area = _____ square units

The ratio of the sides of B to A is $\frac{2}{1}$.

What is the ratio of the areas? Write the answer in the table below.

Dimensions of Rectangle A	Area of A	Dimensions of Rectangle B	Area of B	Ratio of sides of B to A	Ratio of area of B to A
1 unit × 2 units	2 square units	2 units × 4 units	8 square units	$\frac{2}{1}$	

2. Make two more pairs of similar rectangles using the dimensions given in the next table, and complete the table.

Dimensions of Rectangle C	Area of C	Dimensions of Rectangle D	Area of D	Ratio of sides of D to C	Ratio of area of D to C
2 in. × 3 in.		6 in. × 9 in.			
2 m × 5 m		3 m × 7.5 m			

Holt Mathematics

Hands-On Lab
LESSON 5-7A *Areas of Similar Figure, continued*

Think and Discuss

1. What relationship do you see between the ratio of sides of two similar rectangles, and the ratio of the areas of two similar rectangles?

_____

2. If the sides of two similar rectangles have a ratio of $\frac{10}{3}$, what is the ratio of their areas? Explain.

_____

3. If the ratio of two areas of two similar rectangles is $\frac{36}{1}$, what is the ratio of the sides of the similar rectangles?

_____

Try This

1. Use grid paper to draw similar right triangles with the dimensions shown. Find the areas and complete the table.

Triangle A

2   1

6   Triangle B

3

Area = _____ square unit   Area = _____ square units

Dimensions of Triangle A (base; height)	Area of Triangle A	Dimensions of Triangle B (base; height)	Area of Triangle B	Ratio of sides of B to A	Ratio of area of B to A
1 unit; 2 units		3 units; 6 units			

2. Draw two more pairs of similar triangles using the dimensions given in the next table, and complete the table.

Dimensions of Triangle C (base; height)	Area of Triangle C	Dimensions of Triangle D (base; height)	Area of Triangle D	Ratio of sides of D to C	Ratio of area of D to C
4 in.; 1 in.		8 in.; 2 in.			
6 ft; 4 ft		9 ft; 6 ft			

3. How do the ratios of areas and sides of similar triangles compare to the ratios of areas and sides of rectangles?

_____

Holt Mathematics

LESSON 5-8 Hands-On Lab
Scale Drawings and Scale Models

Use with Lesson 5-8

Scale drawings are useful for mapping, construction, and other trades. You can create a scale drawing of your classroom using a tape measure, ruler, and graphing paper. Provided all measurements are converted equally, each portion of your scale drawing should be similar to the actual room.

Activity

Make a scale drawing of a classroom and items with the following dimensions.

Classroom	Six Desks	Teacher's Desk	Aquarium	Chalkboard
15 ft × 20 ft	2 ft × 3 ft	2 ft × 6 ft	6 ft × 2 ft	3 ft by 4 ft
?	?	?	?	?

You can use the squares on graph paper for your model, so that 4 squares = 1 foot. To convert each measurement, multiply the number of feet by 4.

In this case this means that the room would be drawn at 60 squares (15 ft × 4) by 80 squares (20 ft × 4). Convert the other measurements in the table using the same scale.

Classroom	Six Desks	Teacher's Desk	Aquarium	Chalkboard
15 ft × 20 ft	2 ft × 3 ft	2 ft × 6 ft	6 ft × 2 ft	3 ft by 4 ft
60 sq × 80 sq	8 sq × 12 sq	8 sq × 24 sq	24 sq × 8 sq	12 sq by 16 sq

Now sketch the room and items on your graph paper. You can place the items anywhere in the room you wish. Draw the chalkboard to the side so that you can represent it lying flat, and draw an arrow to show where it hangs in the room. An example is sketched on page 60.

Holt Mathematics

Hands-On Lab
5-8 Scale Drawings and Scale Models, continued

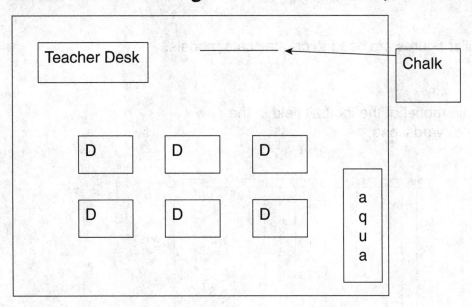

Think and Discuss

1. If you increased the room's length and width by 8 squares each, what would be the dimensions of the new room?

_____

Try This

1. Measure the dimensions of your classroom and some items within the room. Then make a scale drawing in which 3 squares = 1 foot.

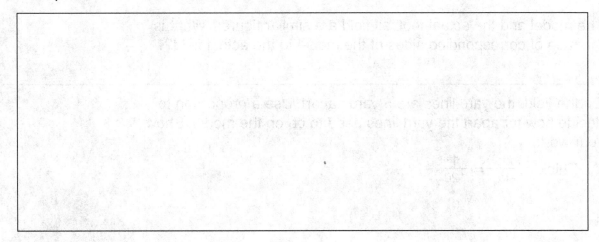

Holt Mathematics

LESSON 5-8A Hands-On Lab
Scale Models

Use with Lesson 5-8

The properties of similar figures are used to create scale models.

Activity

Jaime is making a scale model of the football field in the new stadium. The field is 120 yards long.

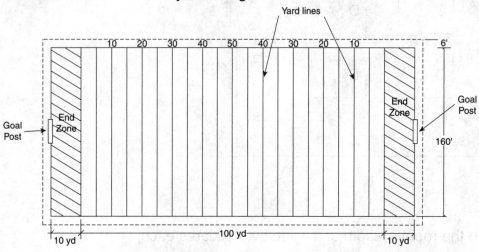

Jaime's model of the field will be 36 inches, or 1 yard, long.

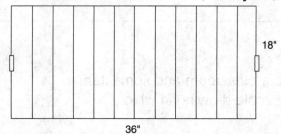

The model and the actual football field are similar figures. What is the ratio of corresponding sides of the model to the actual field?

_____

On the field, the yard lines are 5 yards apart. Use a proportion to decide how far apart the yard lines need to be on the model. Show your work.

Think: $\dfrac{\text{model}}{\text{field}} = \dfrac{1}{120}$

Holt Mathematics

Hands-On Lab
5-8A Scale Models, continued

Think and Discuss

1. Parallel lines on the field are represented by parallel lines on the model. Perpendicular lines on the field are represented by perpendicular lines on the model. Explain why.

   _____

   _____

2. Why is it necessary to use the same units of measurement when you write a proportion?

   _____

   _____

Try This

1. Maxine admires Jaime's finished model and notices that each end zone on the model is 3 inches long. How long is the end zone on the actual field?

   _____

2. Jaime's model has goal posts with the measurements shown. What is the height of the actual ground post and uprights?

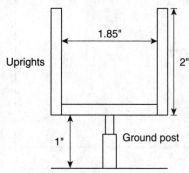

   Ground post: _____

   Uprights: _____

3. Use toothpicks to make a scale model of the goal posts. You can glue the toothpicks on paper to hold them together.

4. What is the scale factor for your goal post model?

   _____

Holt Mathematics

LESSON **Hands-On Lab**
6-1 *Fractions, Decimals, and Percents*

Use with Lesson 6-1

Activity

Changing Percents to Decimals

Remove the percent sign and move the decimal point 2 places to the left.

Example: Change 35% to a decimal.
Step 1 Remove the percent sign.
Step 2 Move the decimal point 2 places to the left.

$$35\% = 0.35$$

Remember:
Percent means "out of 100".
Percent is a part of a whole.

Remember:
Decimals and fractions are also part of a whole.

Jessica scored 87% on her last math exam. The exam contained 40 questions. How many questions did Jessica answer correctly? Make a note card showing how you arrived at your answer.

FRONT

What is 87% of 40?

BACK

Step 1 Remove the percent sign: 87 (or 87.00)

Step 2 Move the decimal point 2 places to the left:
87.00 → . 8. 7 .00

Step 3 Multiply the decimal by the number of which you are calculating the percentage.
0.87 × 40 = 34.8
87% of 40 is about 35.

Holt Mathematics

Hands-On Lab

LE**6** **Fractions, Decimals, and Percents, continued**

Think and Discuss

1. How should a note card be made showing the process used to determine how to change $\frac{7}{33}$ to a percent?

To change a fraction to a percent, find a fraction of the 100 parts, or multiply the fraction by 100 and write a % sign.

Example: Change $\frac{9}{20}$ to a percent.

Multiply the fraction $\frac{9}{\underset{1}{20}} \times \frac{\overset{5}{\cancel{100}}}{1} = 45\%$

FRONT

Convert $\frac{7}{33}$ to a percent.

BACK

Try This

1. Change 15% to a fraction and reduce. _____

2. Change $\frac{5}{8}$ to a percent. _____

3. Find 6% of 150. _____

Holt Mathematics

Name _____ Date _____ Class _____

Explore Percents

Activity 1

Think and Discuss

1. Explain how to model 36.75% on a 10-by-10 grid. How can you model 0.7%? Explain your answer.

_____

_____

_____

Try This

Use a 10-by-10 grid to model each percent.

1. 280%

2. $16\frac{1}{2}$% **3.** 0.25%

4. 65% **5.** 140.75%

64 **Holt Mathematics**

LESSON
6-4
Hands-On Lab Recording Sheet (pp. 340–341)
Explore Percents, continued

Use with Lesson 6-4

Activity 2

Think and Discuss

  1. Explain how to use a percent bar and a quantity bar to find a
  percent of a number.

  _____

  _____

  _____

  _____

  2. Explain how using a percent bar and a quantity bar to model
  finding a percent of a number involves estimation.

  _____

  _____

  _____

Try This

**Use a percent bar and a quantity bar to find the percent of each
number.**

  1. 75% of 36

  2. 60% of 15

 Holt Mathematics

LESSON 6-4 Hands-On Lab Recording Sheet (pp. 340–341)

Explore Percents, continued

3. 135% of 40

4. 112% of 25

5. 18% of 75

Holt Mathematics

Hands-On Lab
LESSON 6-5 *Percent of Increase and Decrease*

Use with Lesson 6-5

You can use a geoboard or dot paper to help you understand the concepts of percent of increase and percent of decrease.

Activity

1. Follow the steps to model a percent decrease.

   a. Make a 4-by-4 square like the one shown at right.

   b. To decrease the area of the square by 25%, first divide the square into four equal parts. (Recall that 25% is equivalent to $\frac{1}{4}$).

   c. Remove one part, which represents 25%, or $\frac{1}{4}$, from the original square to model a decrease of 25%.

2. Follow the steps to model a percent increase.

   a. Make a 3-by-3 square like the one shown at right.

Holt Mathematics

LESSON 6-5 Hands-On Lab

Percent of Increase and Decrease, continued

b. To increase the area of the square by $33\frac{1}{3}$%, first

divide the square into three equal parts.(Recall that

$33\frac{1}{3}$% is equivalent to $\frac{1}{3}$.)

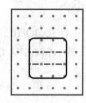

c. Add one part, which represents $33\frac{1}{3}$%, or $\frac{1}{3}$,

from the original square to model an increase of

$33\frac{1}{3}$%.

Think and Discuss

1. Explain why you divided the square in the first activity into four
equal parts.

_____

_____

_____

2. What percent of the 4-by-4 square remains after the 25% decrease?

_____

3. Give an example of a figure that you might use to model a 40% increase.

_____

4. In the second activity, what is the ratio of the area of the new
rectangle to the area of the original square? Write this ratio as a
percent. Then explain what this percent means.

_____

_____

_____

Holt Mathematics

Hands-On Lab

LESSON 6-5 *Percent of Increase and Decrease, continued*

Try This

1. Use a 2-by-2 square to model a 25% decrease.
   Then use the square to model a 25% increase.

2. Use a 3-by-3 square to model a $33\frac{1}{3}$% decrease.

3. Use a 4-by-4 square to model a 50% iincrease.

4. Use the figure at right to model a 50% decrease.

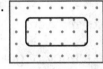

5. Choose a figure to use to model an increase of 10%. Explain
   why you chose that figure.

_____

6. Look at the figures on the geoboard. By what
   percent must you increase the area of the
   figure on the left to get the figure on the right?

_____

Holt Mathematics

LESSON **7-1**

Hands-On Lab
Relative Frequency

Use with Lesson 7-1

You are learning about frequency tables and about relative frequency. For a given category, such as Olympic medals won, a frequency table will show *how often* that category occurs. For example, the table below shows *how many* medals were won in each Olympic city. *Relative frequency* is the percent of the total in each category. The relative frequency would indicate what percent of the total twenty-first century medals were won, for example, in Sydney.

Activity

The table below shows the frequency of individual gold medals won by men from the United States at each of the Olympic Games during the first 5 years of the twenty-first century.

TWENTY-FIRST CENTURY OLYMPIC GOLD MEDALS BY U.S. MEN

Location	Frequency	Relative Frequency
Sydney	67	
Salt Lake City	5	
Athens	85	
TOTAL	157	

Source: http://www.olympic.org

To find the relative frequency of gold medals won by men in Sydney, find what percent the frequency of the group is of the total.

U.S. male athletes competing in Sydney won a total of 67 out of a total of 157 gold medals won by U.S. men during this time period.

$$\text{Relative frequency} = \frac{\text{Frequency of the group}}{\text{Total}}$$

$$= \frac{67}{157} = 0.4268, \text{ or about } 42.7\%$$

About 42.7% of all Olympic gold medals won by American male athletes from 2000 to 2005 were won in Sydney.

Holt Mathematics

LESSON 7-1

Hands-On Lab

Relative Frequency, continued

Think and Discuss

1. How is relative frequency different from cumulative frequency?

   _____

   _____

   _____

2. What must be the sum of all the relative frequencies for a data set? Explain.

   _____

   _____

   _____

Try This

Use a calculator if you wish for these exercises.

1. Find the relative frequencies and complete the table of gold medals won by women in the twentieth century.

2. What is the total of all the relative frequencies in the table? Round the total to the nearest percent.

   _____

3. The number of gold medals won by women of the United States in Olympic games during each decade of the twentieth century is shown in the table below.

Decade	Frequency	Relative Frequency
1900–1909	7	
1910–1919	0	
. 1920–1929	30	
1930–1939	21	
1940–1949	9	
1950–1959	13	
1960–1969	58	
1970–1979	27	
1980–1989	89	
1990–1999	147	
TOTAL		

Source: http://www.olympic.org

Holt Mathematics

LESSON 7-2 Hands-On Lab
Weighted Averages

Use with Lesson 7-2

A *weighted* average is a useful way to give greater importance, or weight, to one or more data values when finding an arithmetic average (mean). For example, your teacher may choose to give the grade for each chapter test twice as much weight as a short quiz. In this Lab, you will use weighted averages.

Activity

Asok received grades of 88, 78, and 90 on quizzes. His grade on the chapter test was 92. If a test is worth twice as much as a quiz, what is his weighted average?

Enter the test grade *twice*. Enter each quiz grade only once. Add up the grades, just as you would do to find the mean score.

$$92 + 92 + 88 + 78 + 90 = 440$$

There were 3 quizzes. The one test counts the same as 2 quizzes. So the total is the same as 5 quizzes. Divide the sum by 5.

$$440 \div 5 = 88; \text{ Asok's weighted average is } 88.$$

Think and Discuss

1. When does a weighted average raise a score? When does it lower it?

_____

_____

_____

Try This

1. On the next chapter, Asok's quiz grades were 86, 76, and 88. His test score was 70. The test score again counts as 2 quizzes. What is the weighted average for Asok's quiz and test scores?

_____

_____

Holt Mathematics

Hands-On Lab

Weighted Averages, continued

2. Find the weighted average for each student if each test score counts the same as 2 quizzes. Then find the mean of the scores.

Student Name	Quiz Scores	Test Score	Weighted Average	Mean
Jamal	100, 100, 95	80		
Nikki	80, 95, 100	100		
SueAnn	90, 90, 90	80		
Jorge	80, 80, 80	90		

3. When is the weighted average sometimes less than the mean? When is it greater than the mean?

_____

_____

_____

4. One season, Max played in 6 basketball games. He scored the baskets shown in the table.

Date	Free-throws (1 point)	2-point baskets	3-point baskets
January 4	1	4	1
January 11	2	3	1
January 25	2	5	0
February 1	0	4	1
February 8	2	6	0
February 15	1	8	1
TOTALS			

a. In the bottom row of the table, write the total number of each kind of basket.

b. Use a weighted average to find the average number of points scored per game for the season.

_____

c. Explain an alternate way of finding Max's weighted average.

_____

Holt Mathematics

Hands-On Lab

Bar Graphs and Histograms

Use with Lesson 7-3

Bar graphs are useful tools for predicting trends and visualizing data. The key steps for making a bar graph are assembling the data, choosing the scale and style of graph, and converting the data into a graph.

Activity 1

The table below contains information about the rainfall levels in Travis County for the past six months. Using graph paper, plot the data as a bar graph. Use colored pencils to make each bar a different color.

January	8 inches
February	13 inches
March	19 inches
April	26 inches
May	15 inches
June	10 inches

Your graph should resemble this:

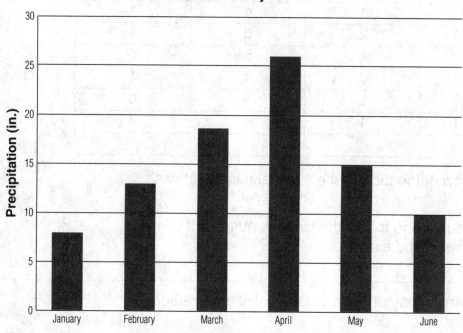

Total Monthly Rainfall

Hands-On Lab

LESSON 7-3 *Bar Graphs and Histograms, continued*

Using your graph, determine the difference between the highest and lowest levels of rainfall.

_____

_____

_____

What pattern does your bar graph show?

_____

_____

_____

Think and Discuss

1. What other types of graphs could be used to plot this information?

_____

_____

_____

_____

2. Why is the bar graph helpful in representing the rainfall data?

_____

_____

_____

Holt Mathematics

Name _____ Date _____ Class _____

Hands-On Lab
Bar Graphs and Histograms, continued

Try This

1. Ask four different people about their daily activities.

   How much time do you spend each day ...?

	Respondent 1	Respondent 2	Respondent 3	Respondent 4
Sleeping				
Studying				
Watching TV				
Exercising				

2. Plot the data from problem 1 as a bar graph.

Holt Mathematics

Hands-On Lab Recording Sheet (pp. 398–399)

LESSON 7-5 *Use Venn Diagrams to Display Collected Data*

Activity 1

Think and Discuss

1. Explain why some of the numbers that were given in the problem, such as 127 and 145, do not appear in the Venn diagram.

   _____

   _____

2. Describe a Venn diagram that has three individual data sets. How many overlapping areas does it have?

   _____

   _____

Try This

Responding to a survey about favorite foods, 60 people said they like pasta, 45 said they like chicken, and 70 said they like hot dogs. Also, 15 people said they like both chicken and pasta, 22 said they like both hot dogs and chicken, and 17 said they like both hot dogs and pasta. Only 8 people said they like all three foods.

1. How many people like only pasta?　　2. How many people like only chicken?

   _____　　　　　　　　 _____

3. How many people like only hot dogs?　4. Make a Venn diagram to show the relationships in the data.

   _____

Holt Mathematics

Hands-On Lab Recording Sheet (pp. 398–399)
Use Venn Diagrams to Display Collected Data, continued

Activity 2

Think and Discuss

1. Tell how many individual sets and how many overlapping areas a Venn diagram of 4 kinds of movie preferences will have.

   _____

   _____

2. Describe what a Venn diagram of student ages might look like. Would there be any overlapping sets? Explain.

   _____

   _____

   _____

Try This

1. Interview your classmates to find out what kinds of sports they like to play. Make a Venn diagram to show the relationships in the data.

2. The Venn diagram shows the types of exercise that some students do.

   a. How many students

   were surveyed? ____

   b. How many students jog? ____

   c. How many students like

   to both bike and walk? ____

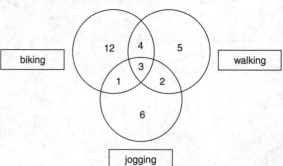

Hands-On Lab
LESSON 7-8 *Explore Scatter Plots*

Use with Lesson 7-8

Look at the graph below. Do you think your shoe size has anything to do with your age? In this activity, you will explore data that may or may not have a relationship.

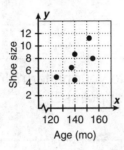

Activity

1. Follow the steps to create a scatter plot.

   a. on a piece of graph paper, draw the horizontal and vertical axes for a graph.

   b. Select two variables from the list below.

   - shoe size
   - length of forearm
   - height
   - month of birth
   - age in months
   - last two digits of phone number

   c. Survey at least six people to find the values for these two variables. Write the information you get from each person as an ordered pair. For example, (show size, last two digits of phone number) could be (7, 31).

   d. Label the axes of your graph with the variables. Then plot the data you gathered as points on the graph.

Holt Mathematics

Hands-On Lab

Explore Scatter Plots, continued

Think and Discuss

1. Do the points on your graph form a pattern? Explain.

   _____

   _____

   _____

2. Do you have any point that does not fit into your pattern? If so, how does this point compare with the other points?

   _____

3. Do the points appear to be almost in a straight line? If so, describe the line.

   _____

   _____

Try This

1. Graph the ordered pairs below. How is the pattern in this graph similar to or different from the pattern in the graph you made in the Activity?

   (1, 2)(2, 2)(2, 3)(3, 4)(4, 3)(4, 5)(5, 5)(6, 4)(7, 6)(7, 8)(8, 7)

   _____

   _____

Holt Mathematics

Hands-On Lab

LESSON 7-9

Choose the Most Appropriate Graph

Choosing the right kind of graph makes data easy to view and understand. Likewise, choosing the wrong kind of graph can make data harder to understand than it would be in the form of simple text or a table. The right kind of graph is the one that suits the kind of data you have collected and the aspect of the data that you wish to emphasize. Depending on what you wish to show, there may be more than one way to display a given set of data.

Activity

Each table of information below has been turned into a graphic display. In each case, identify the kind of display used. Analyze whether it was a good choice, and say why or why not. If the graph was not a good choice, suggest a better one.

1. Price per share of Stock in Scintillating Systems, Inc.

Price per share (dollars)

Year	2001	2002	2003	2004
Price per share (dollars)	78.50	69.40	81.20	75.30

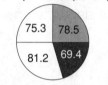

_____

_____

2. Chess Club Yearly Budget

Refreshments	Publicity	Equipment	Miscellaneous
30%	10%	25%	35%

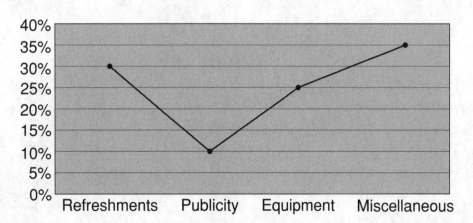

_____

_____

Holt Mathematics

LESSON 7-9 Hands-On Lab

Choose the Most Appropriate Graph, continued

Think and Discuss

1. In each of the following examples, you are asked to choose between two different types of graphic displays. Say what factors would influence your choice.

   a. Bar chart or circle graph

   b. Venn diagram or line plot

2. If you are using a spreadsheet program to make your chart and you choose an inappropriate graph, would you expect to see an error message on your screen?

Try this

Generate a short table of data of any kind. Make two graphic displays, one that is inappropriate and one that is appropriate. Show your data and your two graphs to your classmates, and ask if they can see why one display is a better choice than the other.

Holt Mathematics

Hands-On Lab
Points, Lines, and Planes

Use with Lesson 8-1

The undefined terms, point, line, and plane, are sometimes difficult to understand. Real objects can represent these items and give a clearer understanding of their meaning.

Activity

A piece of paper is often used to represent a plane, but unlike a plane it has borders and depth. The edge of the paper could represent a line, and the corner of the paper could represent a point.

Cut a piece of paper in a straight line across the middle. Now cut one of these halves in half. Continue cutting one of the remaining halves into two pieces until the paper becomes too small to cut. You should now have 14 to 20 pieces of paper of varying sizes.

The smallest piece of paper represents a point. The original piece of paper, the plane, was composed of many of these smaller points joined together. If enough of the points were created and joined end-to-end they would form a line. The lines could then be joined to form the plane.

It is not possible to cut the paper into a small enough particle to accurately represent a point. No matter how small it is cut it could be cut even smaller by more precise equipment. In the same way, the whole paper cannot accurately represent the plane. When the paper was manufactured that piece of paper was actually part of an even larger piece of paper. A geometric plane is perfectly flat and

Holt Mathematics

Hands-On Lab

Points, Lines, and Planes, continued

extends indefinitely in all directions, infinitely larger than the largest piece of paper that could ever be manufactured. A line also extends indefinitely in two opposite directions, perfectly straight and level.

Think and Discuss

Use your observations from the activity to answer these questions.

1. Does a line always contain points? _____

2. Does a plane always contain lines? _____

3. How many points are needed to name a line? _____

4. How many points are needed to name a plane? _____

Try This

1. Draw two points in the space below, as close together or as far apart as you want to. Connect the dots in as many different ways as you can.

2. Measure each line. Which line is the shortest?

_____

LESSON 8-2 Hands-On Lab
Measuring Angles

Use with Lesson 8-2

Key

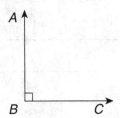

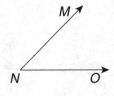

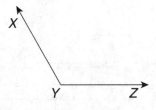

A right angle measures exactly 90°.

An acute angle measures less than 90°.

An obtuse angle measures more than 90°.

Activity

You can measure angles using a protractor.

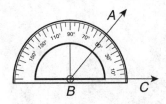

Place the protractor so that the vertex of the angle is at the center of the protractor and one side of the angle is aligned with the 0 on either the inner or the outer scale of the protractor.

Read the measurement of the angle from the protractor.

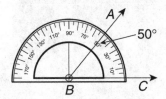

On the same scale, read the number at the point where the other side of the angle meets the protractor. The measure of the angle shown is 50°, so it is an acute angle.

Holt Mathematics

LESSON 8-2 **Hands-On Lab**

Measuring Angles, continued

Think and Discuss

1. Is it possible to determine the measurement of an angle if one
side of the angle is not aligned with 0°? Explain.

_____

_____

_____

Try This

Use a protractor to measure each angle. Write the number of
degrees and classify it as right, acute, or obtuse.

1.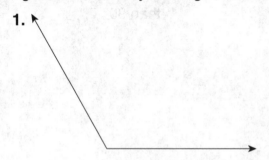

_____

2.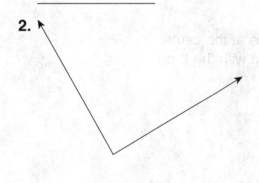

_____

3.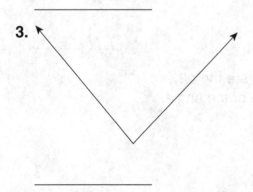

_____

Holt Mathematics

Hands-On Lab Recording Sheet (pp.464-465)

LESSON 8-2

Explore Complementary and Supplementary Angles

Activity 1

Think and discuss

1. Explain how to find the measure of ∠BVC without moving the protractor.

_____

_____

_____

Try This

Use the protractor in Activity 1 to find the measure of each angle.

1. ∠AVC   2. ∠AVZ   3. ∠DVC

_____   _____   _____

Activity 2

Think and Discuss

1. For each type of angle pair, complementary and supplementary, write a rule that relates the angle measurements.

_____

_____

_____

Holt Mathematics

LESSON
8-2
Hands-On Lab Recording Sheet (pp.464-465)
Explore Complementary and Supplementary Angles, continued

Try This

Use a protractor to measure each of the angle pairs below. Tell whether the angle pairs are complementary, supplementary or neither.

1.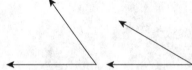

2.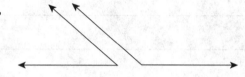

3.

4.

5. How can you tell that the angle pairs in Exercise 4 are supplementary without using a protractor?

_____

_____

6. Use a protractor to find all the angle pairs of complementary and supplementary angles in the figure at right.

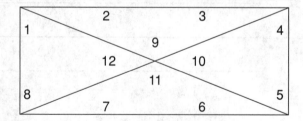

_____

_____

_____

Holt Mathematics

Hands-On Lab Recording Sheet (pp. 456–457)

LESSON 8-3

Construct Bisectors and Congruent Angles

Activity

Think and Discuss

1. How many bisectors would you use to divide an angle into four equal parts?

   _____

2. An 88° angle is bisected, and then each of the two angles formed are bisected. What is the measure of each of the smaller angles formed?

   _____

Holt Mathematics

LESSON 8-3 Hands-On Recording Sheet (pp. 456–457)

Construct Bisectors and Congruent Angles, continued

Try This

Use a compass and a straightedge to perform each construction.

1. Bisect a line segment.

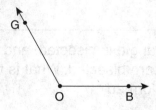

2. Trace and then bisect angle *GOB*.

3. Draw an angle congruent to angle *GOB*.

Holt Mathematics

Hands-On Lab
Constructions

Use with Lesson 8-3

Activity 1: Constructing Congruent Segments

1. Draw a ray with endpoint *C* underneath $\overline{AB}$.

2. Open the compass to the length of $\overline{AB}$.

3. With the same compass setting, put the compass point on point *C*. Draw an arc that intersects the ray. Label the point of intersection as point *D*. The length of $\overline{CD}$ is equal to the length of $\overline{AB}$.

Activity 2: Constructing Congruent Angles

1. Draw a ray with endpoint *S* beside angle *A*.

2. With the compass point on point *A*, draw an arc that intersects the sides of ∠*A*. Label the points of intersection *B* and *C*.

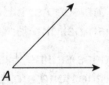

3. With the same compass setting, put the compass point on point *S*. Draw an arc and label its point of intersection with the ray as *R*.

4. Open the compass to the length *BC*, keeping the same compass setting. Put the compass on point R. Draw an arc to locate point T. Draw $\overline{ST}$ through the point where the two arcs meet to complete the angle.

Activity 3: Constructing Parallel Lines

1. Label two points *X* and *Y* on *l*.

2. Draw a line through *X* and *A*.

3. Construct ∠1 with vertex at *A* so that ∠1 ≅ *AXY* and the two angles are corresponding angles. Label the line you just constructed *m*.

Holt Mathematics

Hands-On Lab

LESSON
8-3
Constructions, continued

Activity 4: Drawing a Perpendicular Line

1. Put the compass point on point P. Draw arcs that intersect l at two points, Label the points X and Y.

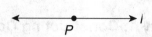

2. Open the compass wider. Place the compass tip on X and draw an arc above point P.

3. Keep the same compass setting. Place the compass point on point Y. Draw an arc that intersects with the arc from step 2. Lable the point where the arcs intersect as point Q.

4. Draw a line through Q and P.

Activity 5: Constructing a perpendicular Bisector

1. Put the compass point on point A and draw an arc that passes through the segment. Be sure the opening is greater than half the length of the segment.

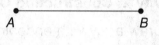

2. Keep the same compass setting. Place the compass point on point B and draw another long arc. Be sure that the new arc passes through the segment. Label the points where the two arcs intersect above and below the segment as X and Y.

3. Draw a line that passes through the segment and through points X and Y. The point of intersection of the segment and the line is M, the midpoint of $\overline{AB}$.

Activity 6: Constructing an Angle Bisector

1. Place the compass point on vertex A. Draw an arc that intersects the sides of $\angle A$. Label the points where the arc intersect the sides as B and C.

2. Place the compass point on point C and draw an arc. Keep the same compass setting. Place the compass point on point B and draw an arc. Be sure the arcs intersect. Label the point where the two arcs intersect as X.

3. Draw a ray from vertex A through point X. $\overrightarrow{AX}$ is the bisector of $\angle A$.

Holt Mathematics

Hands-On Lab

Constructions, continued

Try This

1. With a straight edge, draw a segment. Label the segment $\overline{YZ}$. Construct a segment congruent to segment $\overline{YZ}$.

2. With a straight edge, draw an angle. Label the angle *XYZ*. Construct an angle congruent to angle *XYZ*.

3. With a straight edge, draw a line. Label the line $\overleftrightarrow{YZ}$. Construct a line parallel to line $\overleftrightarrow{YZ}$.

4. With a straight edge, draw a line. Label the line $\overleftrightarrow{YZ}$. Construct a line perpendicular to line $\overleftrightarrow{YZ}$.

5. With a straight edge, draw a segment, Label the segment $\overline{YZ}$. Construct a perpendicular bisector of segment $\overline{YZ}$.

6. With a straight edge, draw an angle. Label the angle *XYZ*. Construct an angle bisector of angle *XYZ*.

Holt Mathematics

Hands-On Lab

LESSON 8-3A *Explore Parallel Lines and Transversals*

Use with Lesson 8-3

Parallel lines are lines in the same plane that never cross. When two parallel lines are intersected by a third line, the angles formed have special relationships. This third line is called a *transversal*.

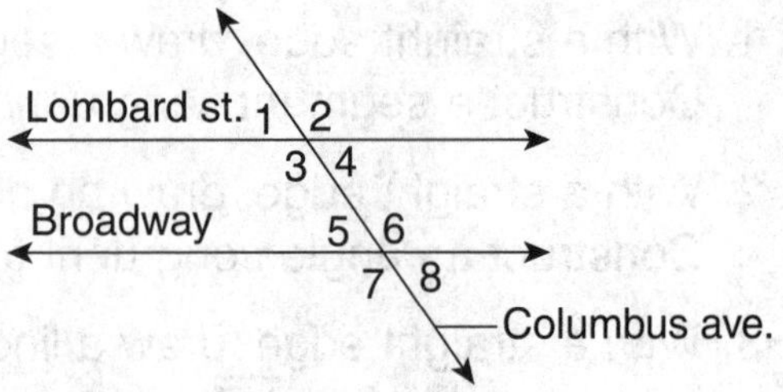

In San Francisco, California, many streets are parallel such as Lombard St. and Broadway.

Columbus Ave. is a transversal that runs diagonal across them. The eight angles that are formed are labeled on the diagram below.

Activity

1. Measure angels 1-8 in the diagram above. Write these measures in your table.

Angle Number	Angle Measure
1	
2	
3	
4	
5	
6	
7	
8	

2. Use the table you completed and the corresponding diagram for the following problems.

a. Angles inside the parallel lines are *interior angles.* Name them.

_____

b. Angles outside the parallel lines are *exterior angles.* Name them.

_____

c. Angles 3 and 6 and angles 4 and 5 are *alternative interior angles.* What do you notice about angles 3 and 6? What do you notice about angles 4 and 5?

_____

d. Angles 2 and 7 and angles 1 and 8 are *alternate exterior angles.* How do the measures of each pair of alternate exterior angles compare?

_____

Holt Mathematics

Hands-On Lab
LESSON 8-3A *Explore Parallel Lines and Transversals, continued*

e. Angles 1 and 5 are corresponding angles because they are in the same position on each of the parallel lines. How do the measures to angles 1 and 5 compare? Name another set of corresponding angles.

_____

f. Add the measures of angles 1 and 2. Now add the measures of angles 3 and 8. What can you say about the relationship of the angles in each of these sets. Name two other angles that have the same relationship.

_____

Think and Discuss

1. $\overleftrightarrow{FG}$ and $\overleftrightarrow{LO}$ are parallel. Tell what you know about the angles that are labeled 1 through 8.

_____

2. If angle 2 measures 125, what are the measures of angles 1, 3, 4, 5, 6, 7, and 8?

_____

3. If a transversal intersects two parallel lines and one of the angles formed measures 90°, discuss the relationship between all the angles.

_____

Try This

Use a protractor to measure one angle in each diagram. Then find the measures of all the other angles without using a protractor. Tell how to find each angle measure.

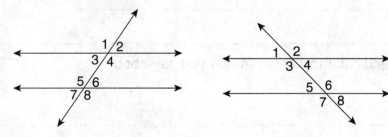

_____

_____

Holt Mathematics

LESSON 8-3B Hands-On Lab
Construct Perpendicular and Parallel Lines

Use with Lesson 8-3B

Activity

1. Construct perpendicular lines.

   a. Draw $\overleftrightarrow{NO}$ and a point *P* above or below it.

   b. Put your compass point at *P* and draw an arc intersecting $\overleftrightarrow{NO}$. Label points *U* and *R*.

   c. Using the same compass opening, draw intersecting arcs from points *U* and *R*. Label the intersection *H*.

   d. Draw $\overleftrightarrow{PH}$.

   What angle does $\overleftrightarrow{NO}$ make with $\overleftrightarrow{PH}$?

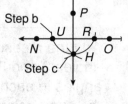

_____

2. Consruct parallel lines.

   a. Draw $\overleftrightarrow{LR}$ and a point *S* above or below it.

   b. Draw a line that intersects point *S* and $\overleftrightarrow{LR}$. Label the intersection T.

   c. Use your compass to construct an angle *USW* at point *S* that is congruent to angle *STR*.

   d. Draw $\overleftrightarrow{SW}$.

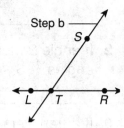

How do $\overleftrightarrow{SW}$ and $\overleftrightarrow{LR}$ relate to each other? _____

Think and Discuss

1. In part 1 of the activity, how would you confirm that $\overleftrightarrow{PH}$ and $\overleftrightarrow{NO}$ are perpendicular?

   _____

   _____

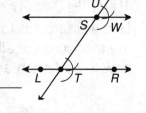

2. In part 2, if $\overleftrightarrow{ST}$ is perpendicular to $\overleftrightarrow{LR}$, what can you say about angle *USW*?

   _____

   _____

Holt Mathematics

Hands-On Lab

Construct Perpendicular and Parallel Lines, continued

Try This

1. Starting with $\overleftrightarrow{MT}$, construct a line segment parallel to $\overrightarrow{MT}$.

2. Starting with $\overleftrightarrow{PS}$, construct a line segment perpendicular to $\overleftrightarrow{PS}$.

Holt Mathematics

Hands-On Lab Recording Sheet (pp. 464–465)
Construct Circle Graphs

Activity

Think and Discuss

1. Total each column in the table from the beginning of the activity.
   What do you notice?

   _____

   _____

   _____

2. What type of data would you want to display using a circle
   graph?

   _____

   _____

   _____

3. How does the size of each sector of your circle graph relate to
   the percent, the decimal, and the fraction in your table?

   _____

   _____

   _____

Holt Mathematics

LESSON
8-4
Hands-On Lab Recording Sheet (pp. 464–465)
Construct Circle Graphs, continued

Try This

1. Complete the table below and use the information to make a circle graph.

On a typical Saturday, Alan divides his leisure time and spends it in the following ways:

Time Spent For Leisure				
Activity	**Percent**	**Decimal**	**Fraction**	**Degrees**
Reading	30%			
Playing Sports	25%			
Working on Computer	40%			
Watching TV	5%			

Holt Mathematics

Hands-On Lab
Drawing Plane Figures

Use with Lesson 8-5

Activity

You can draw polygons using line segments. Polygons are closed figures, so each polygon begins and ends at the same point.

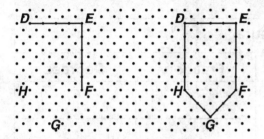

Use a ruler to draw line segments. Each line segment represents one side of the figure. $\overline{DE}$ is one side, $\overline{EF}$ is another.

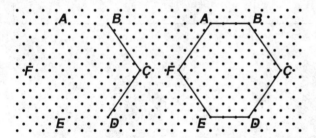

To draw figures with equivalent sides, measure each side with a ruler. Then draw them the same length.

Think and Discuss

1. Is it possible to draw a circle using line segments? Explain.

_____

_____

_____

Holt Mathematics

Hands-On Lab

LESSON 8-5 *Drawing Plane Figures, continued*

Try This

Draw the figure named.

1. Hexagon

2. Pentagon

3. Octagon

Holt Mathematics

Hands-On Lab
Drawing Plane Figures, continued

Try This

Draw the figure named.

4. Heptagon

5. Nonagon

6. Decagon

Holt Mathematics

Hands-On Lab

LESSON 8-5A *Constructions with Polygons and Circles*

A regular polygon is *inscribed* in a circle when all of its vertices lie on a circle that surrounds it.

Activity

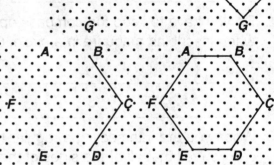

1. Inscribe an equilateral triangle in a circle.

   a. Draw a circle using a compass. Make the circle at least an inch in diameter.

   b. Draw a diameter anywhere inside the circle.

   c. Place the point of your compass at one end of the diameter. Using the same compass opening that was used to make the circle, draw two arcs, one on each side of the point that intersects the circle.

   d. Label the points where the arcs intersect the circle as *A* and *B*. Label point *C* where the diameter meets the circle farthest from the arcs.

   e. Draw line segments to connect the points to form an equilateral triangle

2. Inscribe a square in a circle.

   a. Repeat steps **a** and **b** from part 1.

   b. Construct a perpendicular bisector of the diameter. Then label points *D, E, F,* and *G* where the diameter and its bisector intersect the circle.

   c. Connect the points to form a square.

3. Inscribe a regular hexagon in a circle.

   a. Repeat steps a, b, and c from ❶.

   b. Draw two diameters that each include one of the points where the arcs intersect the circle. Then label the points *L, M, N, O, P,* and *Q* where the diameters meet the circle.

   c. Draw line segments to connect the points to form a regular hexagon.

Holt Mathematics

LESSON
8-5A
Hands-On Lab
Constructions with Polygons and Circles, continued

Think and Discuss

1. Do you have to keep the compass opening the same at all times when inscribing an equilateral triangle in a circle? Explain.

_____

_____

2. Do you have to keep the compass opening the same at all times when inscribing a square in a circle. Explain.

_____

_____

3. When you are intersecting a regular hexagon in a circle, how can you tell that all of the sides of the hexagon are congruent? How does the length of each side of the hexagon compare with the radius of the circle?

_____

_____

4. When you are inscribing a square in a circle, do the sides of the square have the same length as the radius of the circle? Explain.

_____

_____

Try This

1. Inscribe an equilateral triangle in a circle with a 3-inch diameter.

2. Inscribe a square in a circle with a 2-inch diameter.

3. Inscribe a regular hexagon in a circle with a 1.5-inch diameter.

4. Inscribe an equilateral triangle and a square in the same circle with a 4-inch diameter.

Holt Mathematics

Hands-On Lab

LESSON 8-5B *Drawing Squares, Rectangles, Triangles, and Parallelograms*

Use with Lesson 8-5

Rulers, protractors, graph paper, and other tools can help you draw geometric figures.

Activity

Draw the figure described using a ruler and protractor. Label the measurements.

1. a square with one side 1.6 cm long.

2. a rectangle with length $2\frac{9}{16}$ in. and height $\frac{3}{4}$ in.

3. a isosceles triangle with a base of 4 cm and base angles of 40°.

4. a parallelogram with a base of 3 cm, a height of 1.8 cm, and one angle of 60°.

Holt Mathematics

LESSON 8-5B **Hands-On Lab**

Drawing Squares, Rectangles, Triangles, and Parallelograms, continued

Think and Discuss

1. Why must the description include both the dimensions and shape of the figure?

_____

_____

_____

2. How can you use lined paper to draw a parallelogram with a specified height?

_____

_____

_____

Try This

Draw the figure described.

1. a square with one side 1.2 cm long

2. a rectangle with length 3.5 cm and height 1.5 cm

3. an isosceles triangle with a base of 3 cm and base angles of 25°

Holt Mathematics

LESSON
8-6

Hands-On Lab
Constructing an Equilateral Triangle

Use with Lesson 8-6

Using a compass and straightedge, it is possible to construct an equilateral triangle.

Activity

1. Follow these steps to construct an equilateral triangle *ABC* with 3 cm sides.

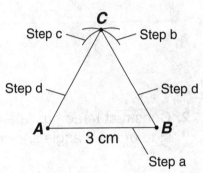

   a. Draw a 3 cm line segment $\overline{AB}$ on a piece of paper.

   b. Place the point of your compass on endpoint *A* and the other end of the compass on endpoint *B*. Draw an arc above $\overline{AB}$.

   c. Without changing your compass opening, position the compass point on endpoint *B* and draw an arc. This arc should intersect the first arc.

   d. Label the point where the arcs intersect Point *C*. Draw line segment $\overline{AC}$ and line segment $\overline{BC}$.

2. Measure $\overline{AC}$ and $\overline{BC}$. What is their measure?

   _____

3. Measure $\angle A$, $\angle B$ and $\angle C$. What is their measure?

   _____

Think and Discuss

1. How do you know that triangle ABC is equilateral?

   _____

   _____

   _____

2. How could you construct a triangle with 3 congruent angles?

   _____

   _____

   _____

Holt Mathematics

Hands-On Lab

LESSON 8-6 *Constructing an Equilateral Triangle, continued*

Try This

1. Construct an equilateral triangle with sides of 1 inch.

2. Construct three equilateral triangles, one with a base on each side of the triangle shown.

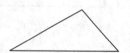

Holt Mathematics

LESSON 8-8

Hands-On Lab

Drawing Geometric Figures

Use with Lesson 8-8

Activity

For exercises 1 and 2, draw a geometric figure based upon the description given. Use a protractor, ruler, or compass as needed. Label all known measures. Then classify each figure (for example, scalene acute triangle).

1. a. The figure has 3 sides.

   b. One angle has measure 50°, and another angle has measure 80°.

   c. The length of the side between these two angles is 3 cm.

_____

2. a. The figure has 4 angles.

   b. Two sides are parallel. The distance between them is 2 cm.

   c. The longest side is labeled $\overline{AB}$, and it is 5 cm long.

   d. Both $\angle A$ and $\angle B$ measure 60°.

_____

3. Describe the following figure, including any known angle measures and side lengths.

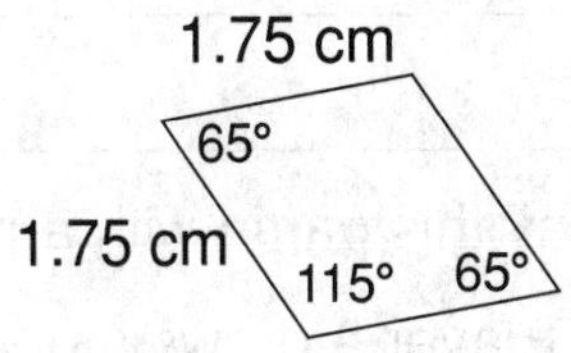

1.75 cm

65°

1.75 cm

115°   65°

_____

_____

Holt Mathematics

LESSON 8-8 Hands-On Lab
Drawing Geometric Figures, *continued*

Think and Discuss

1. If the measures of A and B in exercise 2. are 90°, what if any effect does this have on your description of the figure?

_____

Try This

1. Draw and label a figure using the given information.

   a. The figure is a quadrilateral.

   b. Two sides are 0.75 in. long and two sides are 0.5 in. long.

   c. Three of its angles are each 90°.

_____

_____

2. Which of the following clues are <u>not</u> needed to draw the figure below? What type of figure is it?

   a. The figure has 3 congruent sides.

   b. The figure has 3 congruent angles.

   c. The length of each side is 2.5 cm.

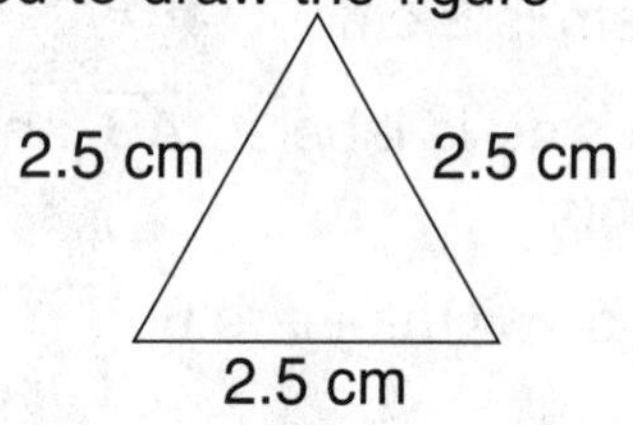

   2.5 cm   2.5 cm

   2.5 cm

_____

_____

3. Play this game with a partner.

   • Player A draws a geometric shape below, but does not show it to the other person. On a separate piece of paper, Player A writes clues that describe both the shape and size of the figure.

   • Player B must then try to draw the shape that satisfies the clues.

   • After one game, players exchange places and play the game again.

   Scoring: If Player B is successful, both players get one point. If not enough information is given to draw the figure, then Player B gets 2 points and Player A gets none. If enough information is given to draw the figure, but Player B draws the wrong figure, then Player A gets 2 points.

Holt Mathematics

Hands-On Lab

LESSON 8-9

Similar Triangles

Use with Lesson 8-9

Two triangles are considered similar if

- their angles are congruent, or

- their sides are proportional, or

- two of the three sides of one triangle are proportional to two sides of the other triangle, and the included angles are congruent.

In this activity, you'll use this information to identify similar triangles.

Activity

1. Work with a partner. On separate piece of paper, each person draws or constructs a triangle with three angles of 60° without looking at the other person's triangle.

   Cut out the triangles and then compare them by placing them on top of each other.

   Compare the lengths of the sides. Are the triangles the same size?

   _____

   Are the triangles similar? Explain why or why not.

   _____

2. On separate pieces of paper, one of you constructs a triangle with side lengths of 3 cm, 4 cm, and 5 cm. The other constructs a triangle with sides measuring 6 cm, 8 cm, and 10 cm.

   Compare your triangle with your partner's triangle. What is the relationship between the sides of one triangle and the three sides of the other triangle? Explain.

   _____

   Are the triangles similar? Explain.

   _____

Holt Mathematics

Hands-On Lab

LESSON 8-9

Similar Triangles, continued

Think and Discuss

1. Chandra says "If two angles of one triangle are congruent to two angles of another triangle, the triangles are similar." Do you agree? Explain your thinking.

_____

_____

_____

Try This

Continue to work with a partner and compare your triangles.

1. Without looking at your partner's paper, draw a triangle with angles of 30°, 40°, and 110°. Cut out the triangles and compare your triangle with your partner's triangle.

   Are these triangles similar? Why or why not?

   _____

   _____

2. On separate pieces of paper, one of you constructs a triangle with a 2 in. side, a 5 in. side, and the angle between these sides measuring 70°. The other constructs a triangle with a 3 in. side, a 7.5 in. side, and the angle between these sides measuring 70°. You are not given the third side length for either triangle.

   Are these triangles similar? Why or why not?

   _____

   _____

   _____

Holt Mathemtics

LESSON 8-10 **Hands-On Lab**
Transformations

Use with Lesson 8-10

Transformation	Description
Translation	The figure moves, or slides, along a straight line.
Reflection	The figure flips across a line, creating a mirror image.
Rotation	The figure turns on a point.
Dilation	The figure is enlarged or shrunk.

In a translation, reflection, or rotation the image is always congruent to the original figure. A dilation enlarges or shrinks a figure, creating an image that is similar to the original figure.

Activity

For Examples 1 – 3, use tracing paper to trace the house on the left or top. Move your copy so it is on top of the house on the right or below. (Fold your paper in Example 3.) Then answer the following questions: How did you move your paper? What transformation did you perform?

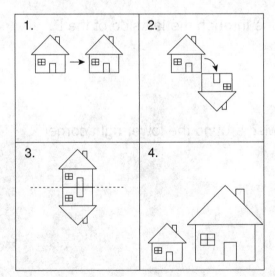

For Example 4, use a ruler to measure corresponding lengths of the original house and its image. How are these lengths related?

Holt Mathematics

Hands-On Lab
Transformations, continued

Think and Discuss

1. Describe some examples of each kind of transformation in everyday life.

_____

_____

_____

_____

Try This

1. Perform each of the transformations of the letter E using tracing paper and folding the paper as needed. Then draw the image.

 a. Translation $\frac{1}{2}$ in. to the right and $\frac{1}{4}$ in. down.

 b. Reflection along a vertical line through the left side of the E.

 c. Rotation through 90° clockwise around the lower right corner of the E.

Holt Mathemtics

Name _____ Date _____ Class _____

LESSON 8-11 Hands-On Lab Recording Sheet (pp. 498–499)

Create Tessellations

Activity

Think and Discuss

1. Explain why the two types of tessellations in this activity are known as translation and rotation tessellations.

_____

_____

Try This

1. Create your own design for a translation or rotation tessellation.

2. Cut out copies of your design from **1** and fit them together to fill a space with your pattern.

Holt Mathematics

Name _____ Date _____ Class _____

Hands-On Lab
LESSON 8-11 *Symmetry*

Use with Lesson 8-11

Symmetrical figures can be thought of as mirror images. For every point that exists in one figure there is a matching but opposite point in the second figure.

Activity

Begin by folding a sheet of paper in half.

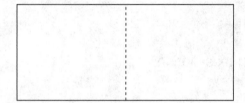

Use scissors to cut the folded paper into the shape of a triangle using the fold as one side of the triangle.

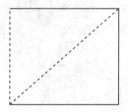

After you have completed the shape, unfold the paper.

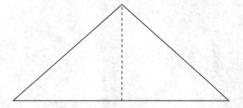

The triangles are symmetrical because if you fold one on top of the other, it covers the other one perfectly (assuming your cuts were straight).

Holt Mathematics

LESSON 8-11 Hands-On Lab
Symmetry, continued

Think and Discuss

1. If you re-fold the paper, can you create a symmetrical rectangle out of the folded paper? Why or why not?

_____

_____

_____

Try This

1. Will the same operation work for a figure with curved lines in it? Fold a piece of paper again as in the above activity, but this time cut out a circle and a heart. Are the shapes symmetrical? Why or why not?

_____

_____

_____

Holt Mathematics

LESSON 9-1 Hands-On Lab
Mass and Capacity

Use with Lesson 9-1

KEY

☐ = 1 gram ☐ = 10 grams ☐ = 100 grams

Activity

Determine the mass of this object.

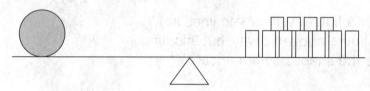

Place weights on the balance scale until the scale is even. Then, count the total mass of the weights on the scale. This determines the mass: 74 grams.

Mass is measured using metric units.

Weight is measured using customary units.

Activity

Find the capacity of this container.

To find the capacity, look at the top of the fluid in the container. Then, read the measurement on the container: $2\frac{1}{3}$ cups.

Capacity can be measured in metric units or customary units.

Holt Mathematics

Hands-On Lab

LESSON 9-1 *Mass and Capacity, continued*

Think and Discuss

1. A tape dispenser is placed in a tray on one side of a balance. Pat uses 82 quarters on the other tray in order to balance the tape dispenser. Let q equal the weight of 1 quarter, and t equal the weight of 1 tape dispenser. What formula expresses the relationship between q and t ?

   _____

2. Examine the measuring devices you have in your classroom (measuring cup, beaker, graduated cylinder). Why is a graduated cylinder a better tool to measure milliliter capacity than a measuring cup? Explain.

   _____

   _____

Try This

Estimate the capacity for each of the following.

1. a glass of milk
   1 milliliter or 1 cup

2. a swimming pool
   500 cups or 500 gallons

3. Estimate how many cups of water will fit into one liter. Then using your measuring cup, fill a one-liter beaker with water. Keep track of how many cups it actually takes to fill the beaker. Compare your actual results with your estimate. Then write a formula that expresses the relationship between cups (c) and liters (l).

   _____

   _____

   _____

4. Estimate how many milliliters of water are needed to fill a 2-cup container. Then using your graduated cylinder, fill a 2-cup container with water. Keep track of how many milliliters it actually takes to fill the container. Compare your actual results with your estimate. Then write a formula that relates milliliters (m) to cups (c).

   _____

   _____

   _____

Holt Mathematics

LESSON 9-1 Hands-On Lab
Mass and Capacity, continued

5. Fill an empty water bottle with sand. Then pour the sand from the bottle into an empty 2-liter bottle. Approximately how many water bottles of sand does it take to fill one 2-liter bottle? Estimate how many water bottles of sand it would take to fill 100 2-liter bottles.

_____

Use the balance or the scale provided by your teacher. Determine the mass of each object using a standard unit of measure.

6. a sock _____

7. a pen _____

8. a shoe _____

9. a stapler _____

10. a small book _____

11. a chalkboard eraser _____

12. an earring _____

13. a box of tissue _____

Determine the mass of each object using the nonstandard unit of measure described.

14. How many pens does a small book weigh? _____

15. How many socks does one watch weigh? _____

16. How many cups of water does one book weigh? _____

17. Estimate how many cups of water two books weigh. _____

18. How many cups of water do two books weigh? _____

19. How close was your estimate in Exercise 17 to your answer in Exercise 18?

_____

20. How many dimes does a quarter weigh? _____

21. Estimate how many dimes two quarters weigh. _____

22. How many dimes do two quarters weigh? _____

23. How close was your estimate in Exercise 21 to your answer in Exercise 22?

_____

Holt Mathematics

LESSON 9-1A Hands-On Lab
Measure Objects

To measure the length in inches of an object, you can use a standard ruler. To measure the length in centimeters of an object, you can use a metric ruler.

Activity 1

1. Use a metric ruler to measure the length of the pencil to the nearest centimeter and to the nearest tenth of a centimeter.

On a metric ruler, the numbered divisions represent centimeters. Since the tip of the pencil is between the 18 cm mark and the 19 cm mark, the pencil is between 18 cm and 19 cm. The tip of the pencil is closest to the 18 cm mark, so to the nearest centimeter it is 18 cm long.

Each centimeter on the ruler is divided into tenths. Since the tip of the pencil is between the 18.1 cm mark and the 18.2 cm mark, the length of the pencil is between 18.1 cm and 18.2 cm. The tip is closest to the 18.1 cm mark, so to the nearest tenth of a centimeter it is 18.1 cm long.

Think and Discuss

1. Which measurement, 18 cm or 18.1 cm, best represents the actual length of the pencil? Explain.

_____

_____

2. Suppose you used a standard ruler to measure the pencil in inches. Would this measurement better represent the length of the pencil? Explain.

_____

_____

Holt Mathematics

LESSON	**Hands-On Lab**
9-1A	*Measure Objects, continued*

Try This

Measure each length, as indicated in the picture, to the nearest centimeter and to the nearest tenth of a centimeter.

1.

2.

_____   _____

Activity 2

1. Usee a standard ruler to measure the lengths of the sides of the rectangle.

2. A standard ruler is 12 inches long, and each inch is divided into sixteenths. Therefore, each division on a ruler represents $\frac{1}{16}$ inch. The length of one of the longer sides of the rectangle is halfway between the 3-inch and 4-inch marks. So, the length is $3\frac{8}{16}$ in., or $3\frac{1}{2}$ in. The length of one of the shorter sides is a little over 1 inch. Since the side ends at the second mark after the 1-inch mark, the length is $1\frac{2}{16}$ in., or $1\frac{1}{8}$ in.

Find the distance around the rectangle.

$3\frac{8}{16} + 3\frac{8}{16} + 1\frac{2}{16} + 1\frac{2}{16} = 8 + \frac{20}{16}$ *Add the whole numbers. Then add the fractions.*

$= 8 + 1\frac{4}{16}$ *Write the fraction as a mixed number.*

$= 9\frac{4}{16}$ *Add the whole number.*

$= 9\frac{1}{4}$ *Write the fraction in simplest form.*

The distance around the rectangle is $9\frac{1}{4}$ inches.

Holt Mathematics

Hands-On Lab

LESSON 9-1A *Measure Objects, continued*

Think and Discuss

1. Use a metric ruler to measure the length of each side of the rectangle to the nearest tenth of a centimeter. What can you conclude about the relationship between an inch and a centimeter?

_____

Try This

Use a standard ruler to measure the length and width of rectangle. Then find the total distance around the rectangle.

1.

2.

Use a metric ruler to measure the length and width of each rectangle. Then find the distance around each rectangle.

3.

4.

Holt Mathematics

LESSON 9-2 Hands-On Lab Recording Sheet (pp. 522–523)
Explore Perimeter & Circumference

Activity 1

Think and Discuss

1. What pattern is made by the points on your graph?

   _____

2. How is the sum of the length and width of each rectangle related
   to the rectangle's perimeter of 18 inches?

   _____

3. Suppose a rectangle has length *l* and width *w*. Write a rule that
   you can use to find the rectangle's perimeter.

   _____

Try This

Use the rule you discovered to find the perimeter of each rectangle.

1. 4 in.
   6 in.

2. 3 ft
   9 ft

3. 5 cm
   5 cm

   _____   _____   _____

Hands-On Lab Recording Sheet (pp. 522–523)

LESSON 9-2 *Explore Perimeter & Circumference, continued*

Activity 2

1. In general, what do you notice about the points on your graph? What shape do they seem to form?

   _____

2. Calculate the ratio of the circumference to the diameter for each of the data points. Then calculate the mean of these ratios. For any circle, the ratio of the circumference to the diameter is a constant, known as *pi* (π). Give an estimate for π based on your findings.

   _____

Try This

1. For a circle with circumference C and diameter d, write the formula that you can use to find the circumference of a circle when you know the diameter.

   _____

2. Use your estimate for the value of π to find the approximate circumference of the circle below.

   _____

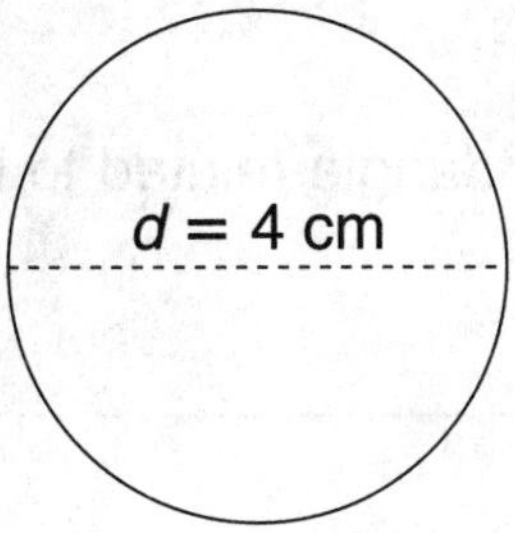

   $d = 4$ cm

Hands-On Lab Recording Sheet (pp. 528–529)

Explore Area of Polygons

Activity 1

Think and Discuss

1. How are the length and width of the rectangle related to the base and height of the parallelgram?

_____

2. Suppose a parallelogram has base *b* and height *h*. Write a formula for the area of the parallelogram.

_____

_____

Try This

1. Does your formula work for any parallelogram? If so, show how to use the formula to find the area of the parallelogram.

_____

2. Explain what must be true about the areas of the parallelograms.

_____

_____

Activity 2

Think and Discuss

1. How are the base and height of the triangle related to the base and height of the parallelogram?

_____

_____

Holt Mathematics

Hands-On Lab Recording Sheet (pp. 528–529)

LESSON 9-3 *Explore Area of Polygons, continued*

2. Suppose a triangle has base *b* and height *h*. Write a formula for the area of the triangle.

_____

Try This

1. Find the area of a triangle with a base of 10 ft and a height of 5 ft.

_____

Activity 3

Think and Discuss

1. What is the length of the base of the parallelogram? What is the parallelogram's area?

_____

2. What is the area of one of the trapezoids in the figure?

_____

Try This

1. Find the area of a trapezoid with bases 4 in. and 6 in. and a height of 8 in.

_____

Holt Mathematics

Hands-On Lab
Area of Parallelograms

Use with Lesson 9-3

All rectangles are parallelograms, but not all parallelograms are rectangles.

Activity 1

Using graph paper, with each square representing 1 cm, draw a parallelogram that has a height (*h*) of 5 cm and a base length (ℓ) of 10 cm.

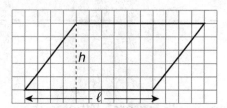

Cut along the dotted perpendicular line. Then arrange the two figures to create a quadrilateral with right angles. You will form a rectangle.

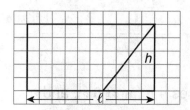

Then cut out enough 1 cm squares to completely fill the parallelogram. Count the number of squares it takes to fill it. Then, check your answer by calculating the area of the parallelogram using the formula you use to find the area of a rectangle: $A = h \cdot \ell$.

Think and Discuss

1. What is the formula for the area of a parallelogram?

_____

_____

Holt Mathematics

Hands-On Lab

Area of Parallelograms, continued

Try This

1. Draw a parallelogram with $h = 9$ cm and $\ell = 15$ cm. Rearrange the parallelogram into a rectangle and calculate its area.

_____

2. Draw a parallelogram with $h = 7$ cm and $\ell = 3$ cm. Rearrange the parallelogram into a rectangle and calculate its area.

_____
_____

Holt Mathematics

LESSON 9-4

Hands-On Lab
Areas of Triangles and Trapezoids

Use with Lesson 9-4

Two congruent triangles or trapezoids can be rearranged to form parallelograms.

Activity 1

On another piece of paper, draw two congruent triangles with a height (h) of 5 cm and a base length (b) of 10 cm.

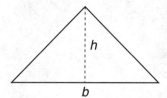

Cut out the triangles and rearrange them as shown to form a parallelogram.

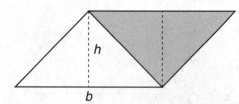

Calculate the area of the parallelogram (A (parallelogram)):

A (parallelogram) $= bh = 5 \cdot 10 = 50$ cm^2

The area of each triangle (A (triangle)) is half the area of the parallelogram:

A (triangle) $= \frac{1}{2}bh = \frac{1}{2} \cdot 5 \cdot 10 = 25$ cm^2

Activity 2

On another piece of paper, draw two congruent trapezoids with $h = 3$ cm and lengths $a = 5$ cm and $b = 10$ cm.

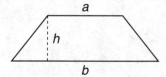
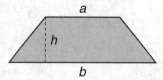

Cut out the trapezoids and rearrange them as shown to form a parallelogram.

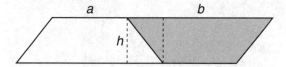

Holt Mathematics

LESSON **Hands-On Lab**
9-4 *Areas of Triangles and Trapezoids, continued*

Calculate the area of the parallelogram (A_P).

$A_P = h(a + b) = 3(10 + 5) = 45$ cm^2

The area of each trapezoid (A_Z) is half the area of the parallelogram:

$A_Z = \dfrac{h}{2}(a + b) = \dfrac{3}{2}(10 + 5) = 22.5$ cm^2

Think and Discuss

1. Look at the two trapezoids below. Trapezoid 1 has $h = 5$ cm, $a = 9$ cm and $b = 4.5$ cm. Trapezoid 2 has $h = 5$ cm, $a = 1.5$ cm and $b = 12$ cm. Do they have the same area? Why or why not?

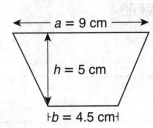

Trapezoid 1

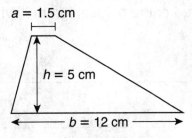

Trapezoid 2

_____

_____

_____

Holt Mathematics

Name _____ Date _____ Class _____

Hands-On Lab

Areas of Triangles and Trapezoids, continued

Try this

1. Draw two congruent triangles with $h = 10$ cm and $b = 4$ cm. Cut them out and rearrange them as a parallelogram. What is the area of the parallelogram? What is the area of each triangle?

_____

_____

_____

2. Draw two congruent trapezoids with $h = 2$ cm, $a = 6$ cm, and $b = 4$ cm. Cut them out and rearrange them as a parallelogram. What is the area of the parallelogram? What is the area of each trapezoid?

_____

_____

_____

_____

Holt Mathematics

LESSON
9-4

Hands-On Lab
Areas of Triangles and Trapezoids, continued

The formula for finding the area can also be used to work
backwards to find the length of missing sides of shapes.

Activity

Use the diagrams and area formulas for triangles and trapezoids to
work backward to find missing measurements by using inverse
operations.

Triangle	Area $= \frac{1}{2} bh$	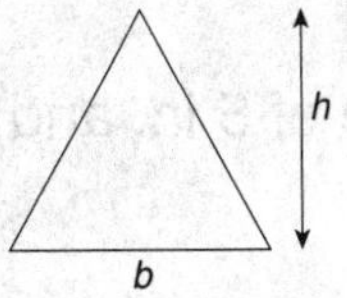
Trapezoid	Area $= \frac{1}{2}(a+b)h$	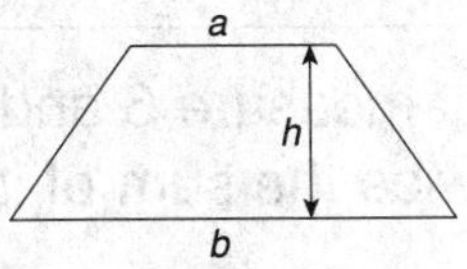

Trapezoid R has an area of 16 in.^{2} and bases that measure 5 in.
and 3 in. What is the height of the trapezoid?

$$\text{Area} = \frac{1}{2}(a + b)h$$

$$16 \text{ in.}^2 = \frac{1}{2}(5 + 3)h$$

$$16 \text{ in.}^2 = \frac{1}{2}(8)h$$

$$\frac{16 \text{ in.}^2}{4} = \frac{4 \times h}{4}$$

$$4 \text{ in.} = h$$

The height of the trapezoid is 4 inches.

Holt Mathematics

Hands-On Lab
Areas of Triangles and Trapezoids, continued

Think and Discuss

1. Explain whether you could find the base and height of a shape if you only knew the area.

_____

_____

Try This

1. A right triangle has a base of 5 in. and an area of 10 in.^{2} What is the height of the triangle?

_____

2. A trapezoid has bases that measure 6 and 9 cm. in length. Its height is 6 cm less than twice the sum of its bases. What is the trapezoid's area?

_____

3. A trapezoid has an area of 34 in.^{2} If the sum of its bases is 8 in., what is the trapezoid's height?

_____

4. A triangle has a base of 10 ft. If its area is 80 ft^2, what is its height?

_____

Holt Mathematics

Hands-On Lab Recording Sheet (pp. 548–549)

Lesson 9-7 *Explore Square Roots and Perfect Squares*

Activity 1

Think and Discuss

1. How does the square root relate to the total number of small squares in a figure?

_____

2. How does the square root in the table relate to the dimensions of each figure?

_____

Try This

Use graph paper to find each square root.

1. 121   **2.** 144   **3.** 196

_____   _____   _____

Holt Mathematics

Lesson 9-7 # Hands-On Lab Recording Sheet (pp. 548–549)
Explore Square Roots and Perfect Squares, continued

Activity 2

Think and Discuss

1. Describe how to use two numbers to estimate the square roots of non-perfect squares without using a calculator.

_____

_____

_____

2. Explain how you can use graph paper to estimate $\sqrt{19}$.

_____

_____

_____

3. Name three numbers that have square roots between 5 and 6.

_____

Try This

Use graph paper to estimate each square root. Then use a calculator to find the square root to the nearest tenth.

1. $\sqrt{19}$ **2.** $\sqrt{10}$ **3.** $\sqrt{28}$ **4.** $\sqrt{35}$

Holt Mathematics

Hands-On Lab Recording Sheet (pp. 554–555)

LAB 9-8 *Explore the Pythagorean Theorem*

Activity 1

Think and Discuss

1. What can you tell about the relationship between the areas of the squares?

   _____

   _____

2. **a.** How does the side length of a square relate to the area of the square?

   _____

   _____

   b. How do the side lengths of the triangle in your drawing relate to the areas of the squares around it?

   _____

   _____

   c. Write an equation that shows the relationship between the lengths of the sides of the triangle in your drawing. Use the variables *a* and *b* to represent the lengths of the two shorter sides of your triangle, and *c* to represent the length of the longest side.

Try This

1. Repeat Activity 1 for other isosceles right triangles. Is the relationship that you found true for the areas of the squares around each triangle?

   _____

   _____

Holt Mathematics

Hands-On Lab Recording Sheet (pp. 554–555)

LAB 9-8 *Explore the Pythagorean Theorem, continued*

Activity 2

Think and Discuss

1. What is the area of each of the three squares? What relationship is there between the areas of the small squares and the area of the large square?

_____

_____

2. What is the length of the third side of the triangle?

_____

3. Substitute the side lengths of your triangle into the equation you wrote in Think and Discuss problem 2c in Activity 1. What do you find?

_____

_____

4. Do you think the relationship is true for triangles that are not right triangles?

_____

_____

Try This

1. Use graph paper to cut out three squares with sides that are 3 units, 4 units, and 6 units long. Fit the squares together to form a triangle as shown at right. Is the relationship between the areas of the two smaller squares and the area of the largest square the same as the relationship shown in Activity 2? Explain.

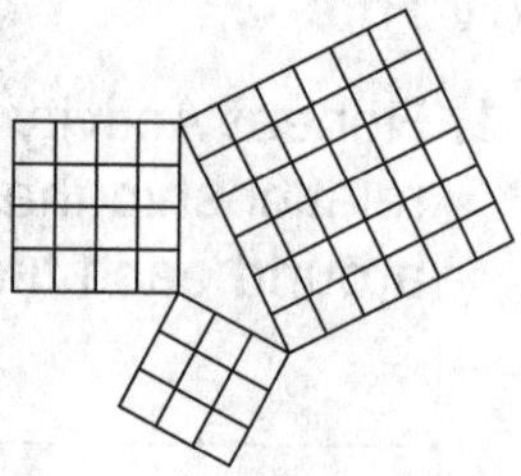

_____

_____

Holt Mathematics

Hands-On Lab Recording Sheet (pp. 554–555)

LAB 9-8 *Explore the Pythagorean Theorem, continued*

2. If you know the lengths of the two short sides of a right triangle are 9 and 12, can you find the length of the longest side? Show your work.

_____

_____

_____

_____

3. If you know the length of the longest side of a right triangle and the length of one of the shorter sides, how would you find the length of the third side?

_____

_____

_____

Holt Mathematics

Hands-On Lab

Lesson 9-ext *Graph Irrational Numbers*

A rational number is a number that can be expressed as a ratio of two integers. All rational numbers can be written as either terminating or repeating decimals. An irrational number is a number that cannot be expressed as a ratio of two integers or as a terminating or repeating decimal.

Every point on the number line corresponds to a real number, either a rational number or an irrational number. Between every two real numbers there is always another real number.

One way to find an approximate value of an irrational number is to locate it between two rational numbers on the number line. The number line below shows the location of several rational numbers.

Activity

1. Copy the number line below. Locate $\sqrt{2}$ on the number line.

Since $\sqrt{2}$ is an irrational number, you must find an approximate value.

Think: 2 is between the perfect squares 1 and 4. Therefore, $\sqrt{2}$ is between $\sqrt{1}$ and $\sqrt{4}$, or between 1 and 2.

To find a closer approximation, you can use decimals rounded to the tenths place.

Think: $1.1^2 = 1.21$

$1.2^2 = 1.44$

$1.3^2 = 1.69$

$1.4^2 = 1.96$

$1.5^2 = 2.25$

Since $1.4^2 = 1.96$, and $1.5^2 = 2.25$, $\sqrt{2}$ is between 1.4 and 1.5.

To find an even closer approximation, you can use decimals rounded to the hundredths place or the thousandths place.

140

Holt Mathematics

Hands-On Lab
Lesson 9-ext *Graph Irrational Numbers, continued*

Think: $1.41^2 = 1.9881$

$1.42^2 = 2.0164$

Since $1.41^2 = 1.9881$ and $1.42^2 = 2.0164$, $\sqrt{2}$ is between 1.41 and 1.42.

Think:

1.411^2	=	1.990921
1.412^2	=	1.993744
1.413^2	=	1.996569
1.414^2	=	1.999396
1.415^2	=	2.002225

So, $\sqrt{2}$ is between 1.414 and 1.415.

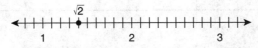

2. Locate $\sqrt{5}$ on a number line.

Think: 5 is between the perfect squares 4 and 9. Therefore, $\sqrt{5}$ is between $\sqrt{4}$ and $\sqrt{9}$, or between 2 and 3.

2.1^2	=	4.41
2.2^2	=	4.84
2.3^2	=	5.29

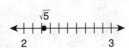

Between 2 and 3

Between 2.2 and 2.3

2.21^2	=	4.8841
2.22^2	=	4.9284
2.23^2	=	4.9729
2.24^2	=	5.0176

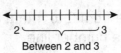

Between 2.23 and 2.24

So, $\sqrt{5}$ is between 2.23 and 2.24.

Holt Mathematics

LESSON 9-ext — Hands-On Lab

Graph Irrational Numbers, *continued*

Think and Discuss

1. Use a calculator to find $\sqrt{5}$. How is this answer similar to the one you found? How is it different? Which is more precise? Why?

_____

_____

_____

2. Is π a rational number or an irrational number? Explain.

_____

_____

Try This

Draw a number line from 2 to 4 that is marked in tenths. Locate each number on the number line.

    1. $3\frac{3}{5}$ **2.** $\sqrt{8}$ **3.** 2.1   **4.** $\sqrt{10}$

    5. $2\frac{1}{2}$ **6.** $\sqrt{11}$ **7.** $\sqrt{6}$ **8.** 2.25

Holt Mathemtics

Hands-On Lab Recording Sheet (pp. 578–579)

LESSON 10-1 *Sketch Three-Dimensional Figures from Different Views*

Activity 1

Think and Discuss

1. How many cubes did you use to build the three-dimensional figure?

_____

2. How could you add a cube to the figure without changing the top view?

_____

3. How could you remove a cube from the figure without changing the side view?

_____

Try This

Use centimeter cubes to build each three-dimensional figure. Then sketch the front, top, and side views.

1.

2.

3.

4.

Hands-On Lab Recording Sheet (pp. 578–579)

LESSON 10-1 *Sketch Three-Dimensional Figures from Different Views, continued*

Activity 2

Think and Discuss

1. Discuss whether there is another step-by-step method for building the above figure. If so, is the result the same?

_____

_____

_____

Try This

The front, top, and side views of a figure are shown. Use centimeter cubes to build the figure. Then sketch the figure.

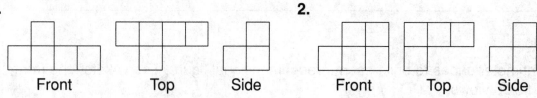

1.   Front   Top   Side   2.   Front   Top   Side

3. The views below represent a three-dimensional figure that cannot be built from cubes. Determine which three-dimensional figure matches the views.

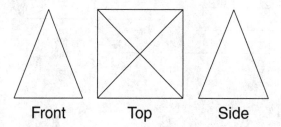

Front   Top   Side

A    **B**   **C**    **D**

Holt Mathematics

Name _____ Date _____ Class _____

Hands-On Lab
Draw Three—Dimensional Figures

Three-dimensional figures have length, width, and height. To draw a three-dimensional figure, you have to choose which view of the figure you will draw.

Activity

1. Draw a side view of a cone with a radius of 1.5 cm and a height of 2.5 cm.

a. From the side, the circular base of a cone looks like an oval. Since the diameter of the cone is 3 cm, draw an oval with a length of 3 cm. Make the top half of the oval dashed.

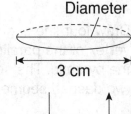

b. Recall that a *perpendicular bisector* bisects a segment at 90° angles. Draw a perpendicular bisector of the diameter, so that one of its endpoints is on the diameter. The length of the bisector is 2.5 cm. This is the height of the cone.

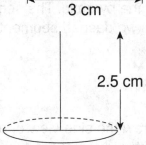

c. Draw two line segments, one from each endpoint of the diameter to the *vertex* of the cone.

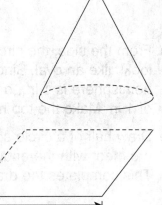

2. Draw the side view of a pyramid with a height of 2.5 cm and a square base that is 2 cm on each side.

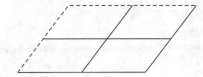

a. From the side, the square base looks like a parallelogram with no right angles. Draw a parallelogram with no right angles. Draw a parallelogram like the one shown. The top and bottom are each 2 cm long. Make the top and one side dashed as shown.

b. Find the midpoint of each side of the parallelogram. Draw two line segments to connect these points as shown.

Holt Mathematics

Hands-On Lab
Draw Three—Dimensional Figures, *continued*

c. From the point where the two segments meet, draw a 2.5-cm line segment perpendicular to the horizontal segment. The length of this vertical segment is the height of the pyramid.

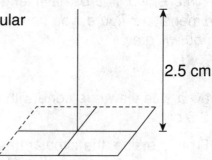

2.5 cm

d. Draw four line segments, one from each vertex of the parallelogram to the *vertex* of the pyramid. The segment that meets the two dashed segments should also be dashed.

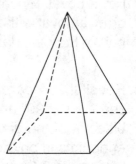

3. Draw the side view of a hemisphere and a sphere with a diameter of 1 in.

Diameter

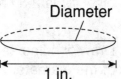

1 in.

a. From the side, the circular base of a hemisphere looks like an oval. Since the diameter of the hemisphere is 1 in., draw an oval with a length of 1 in. Make the top half of the oval dashed.

b. Draw half of a circle so that the endpoints of the arc meet with the endpoints of the diameter. This completes the drawing of the hemisphere.

c. Now draw the other half of the circle. This completes the drawing of the sphere.

Holt Mathematics

Hands-On Lab

LESSON 10-1 *Draw Three—Dimensional Figures, continued*

Think and Discuss

1. How is drawing a cone similar to drawing a pyramid?

_____

_____

2. How is drawing a cone similar to drawing a hemisphere?

_____

_____

3. How does drawing the side view of a cone or pyramid affect the appearance of the base?

_____

_____

Try This

1. Draw the side view of a cone with a radius of 3 cm and a height of 3 cm.

2. Draw the side view of a pyramid with a height of 3.5 cm and a square base that is 2 cm on each side.

3. Draw the side view of a hemisphere and a sphere with a radius of 2 cm.

Holt Mathematics

Name _____ Date _____ Class _____

Hands-On Lab Recording Sheet (pp. 584–585)

Explore the Volume of Prisms and Cylinders

Activity 1

Think and Discuss

1. Describe a shortcut for finding the number of cubes in a rectangular prism.

   _____

   _____

   _____

2. Suppose you know the area of the base of a prism and the height of the prism. How can you find the prism's volume?

   _____

   _____

3. Let the area of the base of a prism be *B* and the height of the prism be *h*. Write a formula for the prism's volume *V*.

   _____

Try This

Use the formula you discovered to find the volume of each prism.

1.

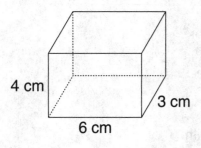

4 cm 3 cm 6 cm

2.

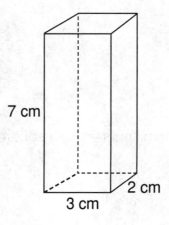

7 cm 3 cm 2 cm

3.

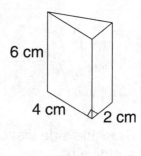

6 cm 4 cm 2 cm

Holt Mathematics

Name _____ Date _____ Class _____

Activity 2

Think and Discuss

1. Suppose you know the area of the base of a cylinder and the height of the cylinder. How can you find the cylinder's volume?

_____

_____

2. Let the area of the base of a cylinder be *B* and the height of the cylinder be *h*. Write a formula for the cylinder's volume *V*.

_____

_____

3. The base of a cylinder is a circle with radius *r*. How can you find the area of the base? How can you use this in your formula for the volume of a cylinder?

_____

_____

Try This

Use the formula you discovered to find the volume of each cylinder.
Use 3.14 for π and round to the nearest tenth.

1.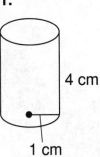
   4 cm
   1 cm

2.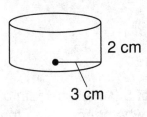
   2 cm
   3 cm

3.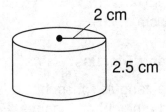
   2 cm
   2.5 cm

Holt Mathematics

LESSON 10-2 Hands-On Lab
Volume

Use with Lesson 10-2

Activity

Find the volume of the rectangular prism.

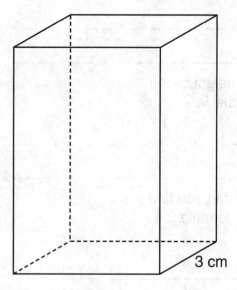

3 cm

The width (w) of the rectangular prism is 3 cm. Measure the length (ℓ) and height (h) of the prism in centimeters.

The length of the figure is 4 cm, and the height is 6 cm.

You can then use a formula to find the volume.

$V = \ell \times w \times h$
$V = 4 \text{ cm} \times 3 \text{ cm} \times 6 \text{ cm}$
$V = 72 \text{ cm}^3$

Think and Discuss

1. A rectangular prism has a length of 5 inches, a width of 3 inches, and a height of 8 inches. Explain whether doubling the length of the prism would double the volume of the prism.

_____

_____

_____

_____

Holt Mathematics

Hands-On Lab

LESSON 10-2 *Volume, continued*

Try This

1. Use the model and a ruler to determine the volume in cubic inches.

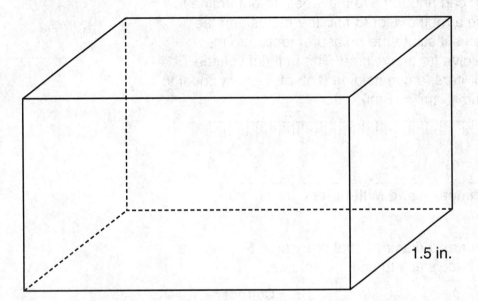

1.5 in.

Volume = _____

Hands-On Lab

LESSON 10-2A *Volume of Prisms and Cylinders*

Use with Lesson 10-2A

Activity

Find a cylindrical soup can and remove the label. To determine the volume of the can, use a metric ruler to find the radius and the height of the can. Then substitute the measurements into the volume formula, and solve for the volume. The units of volume should be given in milliliters (a can holding 8 oz of water is equal to 236.58 ml of water, and 1 cm^3 = 1 ml).

Centimeters and Millimeters

Suppose the soup can has a diameter that measures 5 cm and a height of 10 cm. Use these steps to find the volume.

Cylinder

Step 1 Find the volume of a cylinder using $V = \pi r^2 h$, where r is the radius and h is the height. Use $\pi \approx 3.14$.

Step 2 $V = \pi(2.5)^2(10)$

Step 3 $V = \pi(6.25)(10)$

Step 4 $V \approx 3.14(6.25)(10)$

Step 5 $V \approx 196.25$ cm^3

Step 6 $V \approx 196.25$ ml

Think and Discuss

1. Find the volume of your soup can. Compare the volume you calculated to the volume listed on the soup label. What do you notice?

Holt Mathematics

LESSON **Hands-On Lab**
10-2A *Volume of Prisms and Cylinders, continued*

Prism

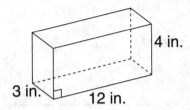

4 in.

3 in. 12 in.

Remember:
A prism is a solid figure that has two parallel, congruent sides, called bases.

Suppose you measured this rectangular prism and determined it had the following dimensions: length of 12 in., width of 4 in., and height of 3 in. Explain, by using steps, how to find the volume of the prism using the formula $V = Bh$.

_____

_____

_____

Try This

1. Write in words the formula for finding the volume of a cylinder.

_____

2. Write in words the formula for finding the volume of a rectangular prism.

_____

3. Use a $\frac{1}{8}$-inch ruler to determine the volume of the cube in cubic inches.

4. Find the volume of the cylinder in milliliters.

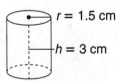

$r = 1.5$ cm

$h = 3$ cm

_____

Holt Mathematics

Name _____ Date _____ Class _____

Hands-On Lab Recording Sheet (p. 596)
Use Nets to Build Prisms and Cylinders

Activity

Think and Discuss

1. What are the dimensions, in inches, of the rectangular prism that you built?

   _____

   _____

2. What is the height, in inches, of the cylinder that you built? What is the cylinder's radius?

   _____

   _____

Holt Mathematics

Hands-On Lab Recording Sheet (p. 596)

LESSON 10-4 *Use Nets to Build Prisms and Cylinders, continued*

Try This

1. Use a net to construct a rectangular prism that is 1 inch by 2 inches by 3 inches.

2. Use a net to construct a cylinder with a height of 1 inch and a radius of $\frac{1}{2}$ in. (*Hint:* The length of the rectangle in the net must match the circumference of the circles, so the length should be $2\pi r = 2\pi(\frac{1}{2}) \approx 3.14$ inches.)

Holt Mathematics

LESSON 10-4 Hands-On Lab
Surface Area of Prisms, Cylinders, and Spheres

Use with Lesson 10-4

The surface area of prisms and cylinders is the sum of their face areas.

Activity

1. Draw the face areas of a rectangular prism. Fold to form a prism.

$h = 10$ cm
$\ell = 5$ cm
$w = 3$ cm

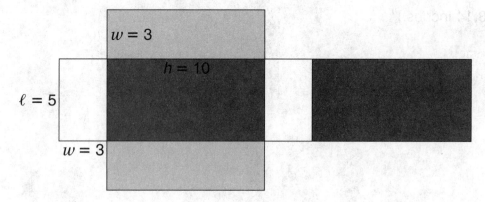

Evaluate the area of the white rectangle.
$A_Y = \ell w = 15$ cm^2

Evaluate the area of the gray rectangle.
$A_R = h\ell = 50$ cm^2

Evaluate the area of the black rectangle.
$A_B = hw = 30$ cm^2

Evaluate the surface area of the prism:
$S = 2A_w + 2A_g + 2A_b = 30$ cm$^2 + 100$ cm$^2 + 60$ cm$^2 = 190$ cm^2.

Holt Mathematics

LESSON **Hands-On Lab**

10-4 *Surface Area of Prisms, Cylinders, and Spheres, continued*

2. Draw the face areas of a cylinder.

$r = 2$ cm $h = 5$ cm

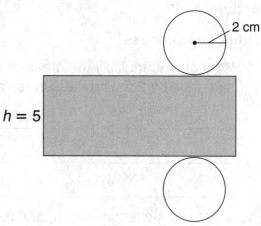

The circumference of the circle (C) is the length (ℓ) of the rectangle.

$\ell = C = 2\pi r = 4\pi \approx 12.6$ cm

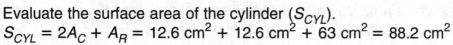

Evaluate the area of the circle.

$A_C = \pi r^2 = 4\pi \approx 12.6$ cm

Evaluate the area of the rectangle.

$A_R = \ell h = (5)(12.6) = 63$ cm^2

Evaluate the surface area of the cylinder (S_{CYL}).

$S_{CYL} = 2A_C + A_R = 12.6$ cm^2 + 12.6 cm^2 + 63 cm^2 = 88.2 cm^2

Think and Discuss

1. Write the formula for finding the surface area of a cylinder. Express the length of the rectangle as the circumference of the circle.

_____

_____

Try This

1. Draw a cylinder with $r = 1$ cm and $h = 10$ cm. Calculate the length of the rectangle and the surface area of the cylinder.

_____

Holt Mathematics

Name _____ Date _____ Class _____

Activity 1

Think and Discuss

1. Why do you multiply the areas of the front face, top face, and side face by 2 to find the surface area of the prism?

_____

_____

_____

2. What are the length, width, and height of the prism in centimeters? What surface area do you get when you use the formula $S = 2\ell w + 2\ell h + 2wh$?

_____

_____

Try This

Use centimeter cubes to build each prism. Then find its surface area.

1.

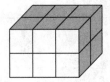

2.

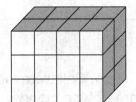

3.

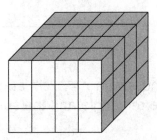

Holt Mathematics

Hands-On Lab Recording Sheet (pp. 602–603)

LESSON 10-5 *Investigate the Surface Areas Of Similar Prisms, continued*

Activity 2

Think and Discuss

1. In **4**, how does the surface area of prism *B* compare with the
   surface area of prism *A*? How is this related to the scale factor?

   _____

   _____

2. In **5**, how does the surface area of prism *C* compare with the
   surface area of prism *A*? How is this related to the scale factor?

   _____

   _____

3. Suppose three-dimensional figure *Y* is similar to three-dimensional
   figure *X* by a scale factor of *k*. How are the surface areas related?

   _____

   _____

Try This

1. Find the surface area of prism *R*.

   _____

2. Prism *S* is larger than prism *R* by a scale factor
   of 4. Use what you discovered to find the surface
   area of prism *S*.

   _____

Prism *R*

Holt Mathematics

Hands-On Lab
Changing Dimensions

Use with Lesson 10-5

How does doubling the height of a cylinder affect the surface area?

Activity

1. Draw the components of a cylinder with $h = 3$ cm and $r = 1$ cm.

Cylinder 1

$S = 2\pi + 6\pi = 8\pi \approx 25.12$ cm^2

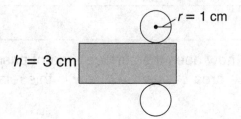

$h = 3$ cm

$r = 1$ cm

2. Now on another piece of paper draw the components of a cylinder with $h_2 = 6$ cm ($h_2 = 2h$) and $r = 1$ cm.

Cylinder 2

$S = 2\pi + 12\pi = 14\pi \approx 43.96$ cm^2

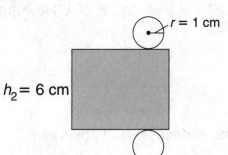

$h_2 = 6$ cm

$r = 1$ cm

Compare the surface areas of Cylinder 1 and Cylinder 2:

Cylinder 1: $S = 2\pi r^2 + 2\pi rh$

Cylinder 2: $S = 2\pi r^2 + 2\pi r2h = 2\pi r^2 + 4\pi rh = 2\pi r^2 + 2\pi rh + 2\pi rh = A_{CYL1} + 2\pi rh$

The surface area of Cylinder 2 has an additional $2\pi \times 3$, which is 6π or ≈ 18.84 cm^2.

Holt Mathematics

Hands-On Lab

10-5 *Changing Dimensions, continued*

Think and Discuss

1. Look at the two rectangular prisms. Do they have the same surface area? Explain.

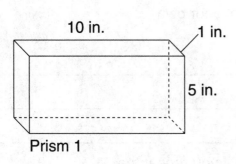

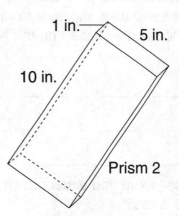

_____

_____

Try This

1. Draw a cylinder with $h = 3$ cm and $r = 2$ cm. What is the surface area of this cylinder?

_____

2. Is it double the surface area of the cylinder with $h = 3$ cm and $r = 1$ cm that you drew in Step 1 of the activity? Why or why not?

_____

_____

_____

Holt Mathematics

LESSON 11-4 Hands-On Lab Recording Sheet (pp. 644–645)
Experimental and Theoretical Probability

Activity 1

Think and Discuss

1. How was the experimental probability of choosing *A* based on all of the combined results, different from experimental probability of choosing *A*, based on the results of your own experiment?

_____

_____

_____

2. How many times would you expect to choose *A* if you repeat the experiment 500 times?

_____

Try This

1. What is the theoretical probability of choosing *A* from five slips of paper with the letters *A*, *B*, *C*, *D*, and *E*?

_____

2. Predict the number of times you would expect to choose *A* from five slips of paper with the letters *A*, *B*, *C*, *D*, and *E* if you repeat the experiment 500 times.

_____

Activity 2

Think and Discuss

1. What do you think is the theoretical probability of choosing *A*-1? Why?

_____

Holt Mathematics

Hands-On Lab Recording Sheet (pp. 644–645)

LESSON 11-4 *Experimental and Theoretical Probability, continued*

2. How many times do you expect to choose *A*-1 if you repeat the experiment 600 times?

_____

3. Explain the difference between the experimental probability of an event and the theoretical probability of the event.

_____

_____

_____

Try This

1. You toss a penny and a nickel at the same time.

a. What is the sample space for the experiment?

_____

b. Predict the number of times you expect both coins to land heads up if you repeat the experiment 100 times.

_____

c. Predict the number of times you expect both coins to land heads up if you repeat the experiment 1000 times.

_____

2. You spin the spinner at right and roll a number cube at the same time.

a. What is the sample space for the experiment?

_____

_____

b. Describe an experiment you could conduct to find the experimental probability of spinning green and rolling 6 at the same time.

_____

_____

Holt Mathematics

Hands-On Lab
Comparing Experimental and Theoretical Probability

Use with Lesson 11-4

KEY

A number cube contains the numbers 1 through 6 on each side. You can use a number cube to compute experimental and theoretical probabilities.

Activity

Roll a number cube 30 times. Record your results in the space below.

_____

_____

_____

From your results, compute the experimental probability of getting a 1.

Count the number of ones in your results.

There were _____ ones in my results

Thus, the probability is _____, which reduces to _____.

Compute the theoretical probability of getting a 1.

Find the total possible outcomes.

On a six-sided die, there are six possible outcomes.

Find the number of favorable outcomes.

Only getting a 1 is favorable, so there is one favorable outcome.

Write the fraction.

The fraction is $\frac{1}{6}$.

Holt Mathematics

Hands-On Lab

Comparing Experimental and Theoretical Probability, continued

Compare your results for the experimental and theoretical probability.

Are your results the same for both?

_____

_____

Think and Discuss

1. In the Activity, how many ones would you theoretically expect? Explain.

_____

_____

2. Why are the experimental and theoretical probabilities of an event often different?

_____

_____

_____

_____

Holt Mathematics

Hands-On Lab

Comparing Experimental and Theoretical Probability, continued

Try This

1. Toss the number cube 30 times. Record your results below.

_____

_____

_____

2. In the chart below, write the theoretical probability of each event. Then compute the experimental probability, based on your results.

Event: Probability of getting...	Theoretical Probability	Experimental Probability
a 6		
an even number		
a number less than 3		

3. Explain how your experimental probabilities differed from the theoretical.

_____

_____

_____

_____

Holt Mathematics

Hands-On Lab
11-5 Probability With and Without Replacement

Use with Lesson 11-5

KEY

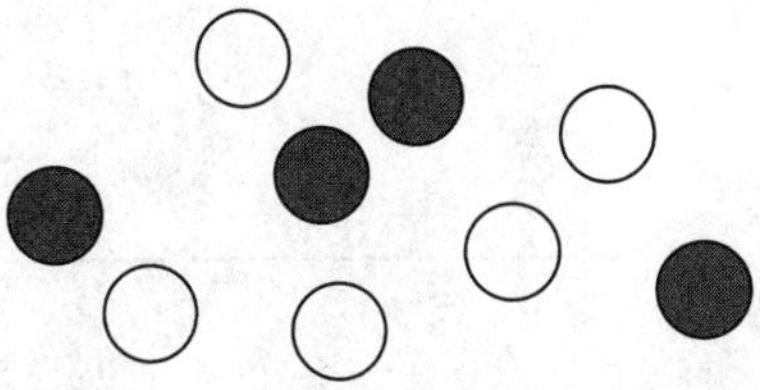

You can find the probability of what color ball will be drawn from the balls above. You can also determine the probability of what color a second ball will be. The second probability depends on whether you replace the first ball or keep it separate from the group.

Activity

A bag contains 4 dark balls and 5 light balls (as shown above).

1. You draw one ball. What is the probability it is light? _____

2. Assume you draw one light ball. and put it back in the bag. Find the probability that a second ball drawn will be light.

After drawing and replacing a light ball, how many light balls will be in the bag?

_____

After drawing and replacing a light ball, how many total balls will be in the bag?

_____

Write a fraction for the probability.

_____

3. Assume you draw one light ball and put it aside. In this situation, find the probability that a second ball drawn will be light.

After removing a light ball, how many light balls will be in the bag?

_____

Holt Mathematics

Hands-On Lab
Probability With and Without Replacement, continued

After removing a light ball, how many total balls will be in the bag?

_____

Write a fraction for the probability.

_____

Think and Discuss

1. Explain what is meant by drawing "with replacement" and "without replacement."

_____

_____

_____

_____

2. Why does the probability change when an object is drawn from a group without replacement?

_____

_____

_____

Try This

A bag contains the following beans: 2 black, 5 white, 4 light gray, 4 dark gray.

Answer each question. Write all answers in simplest form.

1. You draw one bean. What is the probability it is black?

_____

2. You draw one bean. What is the probability it is white? _____

3. You draw a white bean. Since you do not like white, you put it back in the bag and draw another. What is the probability the

second bean is dark gray? _____

Hands-On Lab
11-6 *Pascal's Triangle*

REMEMBER:

- Probability is the likelihood of an event occurring.

- A combination is an arrangement of items or events in which order is not important.

The triangular arrangement of numbers below is called **Pascal'sTriangle**. Each row starts and ends with 1. Each other number in the triangle is the sum of the two numbers above it.

$$1$$
$$1 \quad 1$$
$$1 \quad 2 \quad 1$$
$$1 \quad 3 \quad 3 \quad 1$$
$$1 \quad 4 \quad 6 \quad 4 \quad 1$$
$$1 \quad 5 \quad 10 \quad 10 \quad 5 \quad 1 \quad 4 = 3 + 1$$

You can use Pascal's Triangle to solve problems involving probability.

Activity

1. Geri, Jan, Kathy, Annie, and Mia are on a women's bobsled team. Only two women can race at a time. How many pairings of bobsledders are possible?

   Write each name on a separate card. You will need four cards for each name. Show all of the possible pairings of bobsledders.

   Each pair of bobsledders shown is different. So there are 10 possible pairings of bobsledders.

Holt Mathematics

Name _____ Date _____ Class _____

Hands-On Lab

Pascal's Triangle, continued

Each pairing is a **combination**, because the order is not important.
The following possible combinations can be expressed using the
following notation:

Total number of people $\longrightarrow {}_5C_2 \longleftarrow$ Number of people in each combination

You can use Pascal's Triangle to find the value of ${}_5C_2$ or any
other combination.

a. Copy Pascal's Triangle. Label the rows and columns
as shown.

Column 0
Row 0 → 1   Column 1
Row 1 → 1   1   Column 2
Row 2 → 1   2   1   Column 3
Row 3 → 1   3   3   1   Column 4
Row 4 → 1   4   6   4   1   Column 5
Row 5 → 1   5   10   10   5   1   Column 6
Row 6 → 1   6   15   20   15   6   1

b. To find the value of ${}_5C_2$, look at where row 5 and column 2
intersect.

Column 0
Row 0 → 1   Column 1
Row 1 → 1   1   Column 2
Row 2 → 1   2   1   Column 3
Row 3 → 1   3   3   1   Column 4
Row 4 → 1   4   6   4   1   Column 5
Row 5 → 1   5   10   10   5   1   Column 6
Row 6 → 1   6   15   20   15   6   1

Holt Mathematics

Hands-On Lab

Pascal's Triangle, continued

Think and Discuss

1. In Step 1 of the activity, why is the order of the bobsledders not important?

_____

_____

2. Complete rows 7 and 8 in Pascal's Triangle.

_____

_____

3. What are some patterns that you see in Pascal's Triangle?

_____

_____

4. Find $_3C_3$, $_2C_2$, $_6C_6$, and $_4C_4$. What do you notice? Explain.

_____

_____

5. Ten students are on the basketball team, but only 5 can play at a time. Use Pascal's Triangle to find the number of possible combinations of players.

_____

Try This

Use Pascal's Triangle to find the number of combinations.

1. $_3C_2$ _____   **2.** $_3C_1$ _____   **3.** $_6C_4$ _____

4. $_5C_5$ _____   **5.** $_7C_4$ _____   **6.** $_6C_3$ _____

7. $_6C_1$ _____   **8.** $_4C_2$ _____

Holt Mathematics

LESSON 11-7 Hands-On Lab
Set Theory

A set is any well-defined collection of objects. These objects could be persons, coins, numbers, or any other collection of objects. In mathematics, commonly used sets include the natural numbers, integers, rational numbers and real numbers.

Activity

Obtain a sack of marbles from your teacher.

1. List the characteristics of the marbles. Include as many characteristics as you can think of.

Characteristics of Marbles
Possible characteristics include color, size, mass or weight, patterns, materials, shape

2. Compare your list to a classmate's list. If your classmate thought of any charscteristics you did not think of, add those to your list. Continue comparing with other classmates until your list is complete. Call this your master list.

3. Divide the marbles up into groups with similar characteristics based on your master list. Most marbles could be assigned to more than one group. Make new groups for these marbles, listing all the characteristics that the new groups have. Continue until all of your marbles are in groups and each group contains only marbles with the same characteristics.

Holt Mathematics

Hands-On Lab
LESSON 11-7 *Set Theory, continued*

4. Arrange your groups of marbles together to form groups of groups of marbles. For example, if you have red plastic marbles, blue plastic marbles, and clear plastic marbles, they all belong to the group "plastic marbles." Continue until all of the groups have been assigned to a bigger group. Then group those groups into even bigger groups. Continue until all of the groups have been assigned to larger groups.

For example:

Marbles									
Plastic marbles					Glass marbles				
Big plastic marbles			Small plastic marbles		Big glass marbles			Small glass marbles	
blue	white	clear	blue and white	blue	red	white	green	red	white

Complete.

Think and Discuss

1. Suppose you have 10 plastic marbles, 5 are big and 5 are small. The big marbles are a **subset** of your plastic marbles. Some of the big marbles are blue and some of the small marbles are blue. Are all the blue marbles a subset of your marbles? _____

Holt Mathematics

Hands-On Lab
11-7 Set Theory, continued

2. Draw a diagram showing your 10 plastic marbles, 5 big ones and 5 small ones. Color 3 of the big marbles blue and color 4 of the small marbles blue. Draw a circle around all the blue marbles. The subset of blue marbles you have just circled froms an **intersection** of the sets of blue marbles and big marbles and an intersection of the sets of blue marbles and small marbles. The intersection of two sets includes all the objects that belong in both sets. Now color the rest of the marbles red. Do the red marbles form intersections with the sets of big marbles and small marbles?

3. The union of two sets is all the objects that belong to either set. What is the union of the big blue marbles and the big red marbles?

_____

_____

What is the union of the big marbles and the small marbles?

_____

_____

Try This

1. Set **A** includes the numbers 0, 1, 2, 3, 4, 5, 6, and 7. Set **B** includes 5, 6, 7, 8, 9, and 10. What is the union of **A** and **B**?

_____

_____

2. What is the intersection of **A** and **B**?

_____

Holt Mathematics

LESSON **Hands-On Lab**
11-7A *Graph Theory*

Activity

1. Tanya was shown the following 3 points and asked to draw a path that starts at *A*, goes through the other two points once, and returns to *A* without picking up her pencil.

She drew the following path:

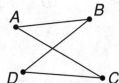

2. Then Tanya was given 4 points and asked to draw 2 different paths, each starting at *A*, going through each other point once, and returning to *A* without picking up her pencil.

She drew the following paths:

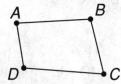
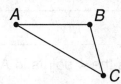

Draw a third path, following the same rules as Tanya. Note that reversing the order in which you select points doesn't change a path. For example, the path from *A* to *B* to *C* to *D* to *A* is the same as the path from *A* to *D* to *C* to *B* to *A*.

Holt Mathematics

Hands-On Lab

Graph Theory, continued

Think and Discuss

1. Is there another path Tanya could have drawn between the 3 opoints, following the same rules? Justify your answer.

_____

_____

2. In Step 2, when Tanya was connecting 4 points, if she started and ended each path at point B, C, or D, would the number of possible paths that could be drawn change? Explain.

_____

_____

3. Can a fourth path be drawn that connects the 4 points in Activity, part 2? Justify your answer.

_____

_____

_____

_____

```
        B              B              B
      C            C          C
  A          A          A          A
                                          C
  E      D    E        D    E        D
```

Try This

1. For each group of five vertices, draw a path according to the rules from the Activity.

2. How many paths can be drawn with 5 vertices?

_____

3. For each group of six vertices, draw a path.

```
        B              B              B
      C            C          C
  A          A          A
  F      D    F        D    F        D
     E          E          E
```

Holt Mathematics

LESSON 12-1 Hands-On Lab Recording Sheet (pp. 676–677)

Model of Two-Step Equations

Activity

Think and Discuss

1. When you add a value to one side of the equation, why do you also have to add the same value to the other side?

_____

_____

2. When you solved $3n + 6 = -15$ in the activity, why were you able to remove six yellow unit tiles and six red unit tiles from the left side of the equation?

_____

3. Model and solve $3x - 5 = 10$. Explain each step.

_____

_____

_____

_____

_____

_____

4. How would you check the solution to $3n + 6 = -15$ using algebra tiles?

_____

_____

_____

Holt Mathematics

Name _____ Date _____ Class _____

Hands-On Lab Recording Sheet (pp. 676–677)

Model of Two-Step Equations, continued

Try This

Use algebra tiles to model and solve each equation.

1. $4 + 2x = 20$ **2.** $3r + 7 = -8$ **3.** $-4m + 3 = -25$

_____   _____   _____

4. $-2n - 5 = 17$ **5.** $10 = 2j - 4$ **6.** $5 + r = 7$

_____   _____   _____

7. $4h + 2h + 3 = 15$ **8.** $-3g = 9$ **9.** $5k + (-7) = 13$

_____   _____   _____

Holt Mathematics

Hands-On Lab

LESSON 12-3

Solving Equations with Multiple Steps

Use with Lesson 12-3

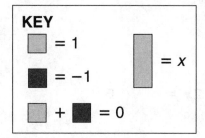

KEY

$\square$ = 1

$\blacksquare$ = −1

$\square$ + $\blacksquare$ = 0

$\mathbf{|}$ = x

REMEMBER:
It will not change the value of an expression if you add or remove zero.

Algebra tiles can help you solve equations.

Activity

To solve the equation $3x - 2 = x + 4$, you need x alone on one side of the equal sign. You can add or remove tiles as long as you add the same amount or remove the same amount on both sides.

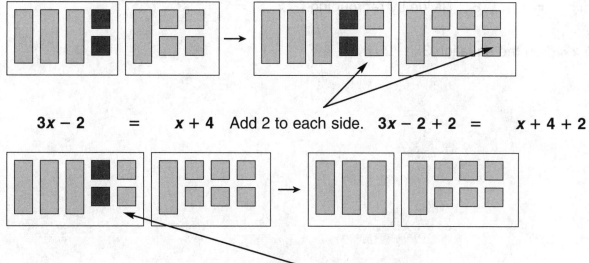

$3x - 2$ $=$ $x + 4$ Add 2 to each side. $3x - 2 + 2$ $=$ $x + 4 + 2$

$3x - 2 + 2$ $=$ $x + 4 + 2$ Combine tiles. $3x$ $=$ $x + 6$

Holt Mathematics

Hands-On Lab

Solving Equations with Multiple Steps, continued

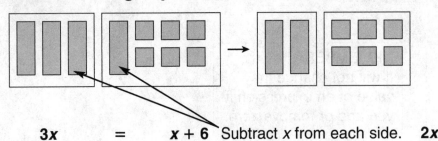

3x   **=**   **x + 6** Subtract x from each side.   **2x =**   **6**

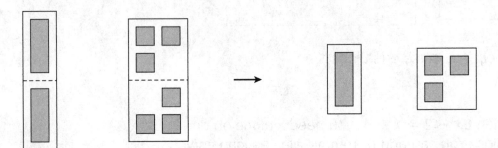

2x   **=**   **6**   Divide by regrouping.   **x**   **=**   **3**

So, $x = 3$ in the equation $3x - 2 = x + 4$.

Holt Mathematics

LESSON 12-3 Hands-On Lab
Solving Equations with Multiple Steps, *continued*

Think and Discuss

1. Describe the steps required to get x alone on one side of the equation $4x + 5 = 25$.

   _____

   _____

2. Subtracting tiles is the same as what other operation?

   _____

3. Summarize the steps required to solve an equation that has occurrences of the variable on both sides.

   _____

   _____

4. What is the first step in solving an equation such as $x - 9 = 4x$?

   _____

5. What operation is the inverse of multiplication?

   _____

Try This

Use algebra tiles to model and solve each equation.

1. $2x - 7 = 11$ _____

Holt Mathematics

LESSON 12-3

Hands-On Lab

Solving Equations with Multiple Steps, continued

2. $2x + 5 = x - 8$ _____

3. $3x + 3 = 4x + 4$ _____

4. $3x + 2 = -7$ _____

Holt Mathematics

Hands-On Lab

LESSON 12-3 *Solving Equations with Multiple Steps, continued*

5. $3x + (-4) = 8$ _____

6. $x - 6 = 2x$ _____

7. $2x + (-1) = -11$ _____

8. $4x - 7 = -5 + 2x$ _____

Holt Mathematics

LESSON 12-6 Hands-On Lab
Solving Inequalities

Use with Lesson 12-6

KEY

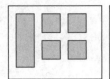

REMEMBER:
It will not change the
value of an expression if
you add or remove zero.

Algebra tiles can also help you solve inequalities.

Activity

Solving inequalities is similar to solving equations. You must get the
variable alone on one side of the inequality sign. You can add or
remove tiles as long as you add the same amount or remove the
same amount on both sides. Solve the inequality $x + 4 < 7$.

$x + 4$ **$<$**   **7** Remove 4 tiles from each side.   **x**   **$<$**   **3**

1. Use algebra tiles to model and solve each inequality.
a. $x + 1 < 6$ **b.** $x + 2 < 7 + 1$ **c.** $x + 3 > 9$ **d.** $x + 5 > 3$

_____   _____   _____   _____

If the inequality includes negative values, you can add tiles to each
side. Solve the inequality $x + (-4) < 5$.

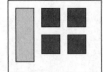   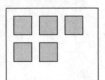   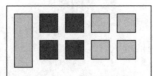   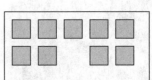

$x + (-4)$ **$<$**   **5** Add 4 tiles to each side.   **$x + (-4) + 4$** **$<$**   **$5 + 4$**

Holt Mathematics

LESSON 12-6

Hands-On Lab
Solving Inequalities, continued

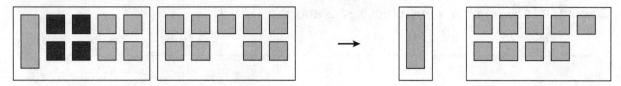

$x + (-4) + 4 \quad < \quad 5 + 4$ Combine terms $x \quad < \quad 9$

2. Use algebra tiles to model and solve each inequality.

a. $x + (-1) < 7$ **b.** $x + (-9) < 3$ **c.** $x + (-3) > -1$ **d.** $x + (-6) > -4$

_____   _____   _____   _____

Both sides of inequalities can be multiplied or divided by the same number. Solve the inequality $3x < 9$.

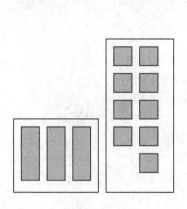 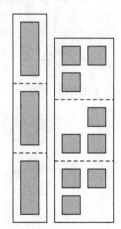

$3x \quad < 9$ Regroup $x \quad < \quad 3$

3. Use algebra tiles to model and solve the following equations.

a. $2x < 2$ **b.** $4x < 12$ **c.** $3x > -9$ **d.** $5x > 10$

_____   _____   _____   _____

Think and Discuss

1. How are inequalities different from equations?

_____

_____

2. If $a < b$ and $b < c$, then what is the relation between a and c?

_____

_____

Holt Mathematics

LESSON
12-6 # Hands-On Lab
Solving Inequalities, continued

3. Is there any number x such that $x < 3$ and $x > 3$?

_____

_____

4. What is the first step in solving an inequality such as $3x - 9 > 6$?

_____

_____

5. Describe the steps required to get x alone on one side of the inequality $4x + 5 < 25$.

_____

_____

Try This

Use algebra tiles to model and solve each inequality.

1. $x - 4 > 6$ _____

2. $x - 1 < 3$ _____

3. $x + 3 > 6$ _____

Holt Mathematics

Hands-On Lab

Solving Inequalities, continued

4. $x + (-4) > 1$ _____

5. $x + (-8) > 1$ _____

6. $x - 6 < 2$ _____

7. $2x > 12$ _____

8. $4x < 8$ _____

Holt Mathematics

Answer Key

Hands-On Lab 1-2
Think and Discuss

1. Add the exponents to get 5^{120}.
2. Subtract the exponents to get 5^{80}.
3. An exponent is defined as a repeated factor.
4. 3^8 because $(3^4)^2$ means $(3^4) \cdot (3^4)$.

Try This

1. 4^8
2. 6^5
3. 3^8
4. 5^3
5. 2^5
6. 7^1
7. 4^{12}
8. 2^{16}
9. 5^6

Hands-On Lab 1-4
Activity

59,000; 57,000; 1.7%

438,000; 432,000; 0.7%

1. $\dfrac{1000}{58,000} \approx 0.017 \times 100 = 1.7\%$
2. $\dfrac{3000}{435,000} \approx 0.007 \times 100 = 0.7\%$

Think and Discuss

1. Because 1000 is a larger percent of 58,000 than 1000 is of 152,000.
2. Because 5000 is a smaller percent of 435,000 than 1000 out of 58,000.
3. Because the ratios of the errors to the size of the populations are the same.
4. Larger errors don't necessarily mean larger relative errors, and smaller errors don't necessarily mean smaller relative errors.
5. An error on its own may seem small but is actually large compared to the total amount. At the same time, an error may seem large but actually is small compared to the total amount.

Try This

1. 0.4%
2. Answers will vary.
3. Answers will vary.

Hands-On Lab 1-9
Activity

$6x$; 5

x^2; $3x$; 4

Think and Discuss

1. The Commutative Property of Addition
2. Both terms are represented by the same size tile: 2 rectangles is 5 rectangles.
3. Think $2x + 3x = (2 + 3)x$, or $5x$.

Try This

1.

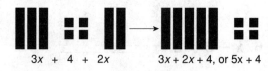

$3x + 4 + 2x \qquad 3x + 2x + 4$, or $5x + 4$

2. $x^2 + 3x + 1$
3. $6x + 6$
4. $x^2 + 4x + 7$
5. $3x^2 + 4x + 1$

Hands-On Lab 1-10
Think and Discuss

1. The values of both sides of the equals sign would not be the same and the equation would be false.
2. Yes because multiplication is repeated addition and you can add the same value to both sides of the equation.

Try This

1. 13
2. 6
3. 10
4. 26
5. 17
6. 22

Holt Mathematics

Answer Key

Hands-On Lab Recording Sheet 1-11
Think and Discuss

1. subtraction; division
2. Answers will vary.

Try This

1. $x = 4$
2. $n = 8$
3. $r = 8$
4. $n = 5$
5. $y = 7$
6. $r = 4$
7. $w = 2$
8. $p = 3$

Hands-On Lab Recording Sheet 2-2
Think and Discuss

1. Yes; $8 + (-3)$ and $-3 + 8$ will give the same answer. Addition is a Commutative operation.
2. negative
3. positive
4. The sign of the answer is the same as the sign of the number that is farther from zero. $7 + (-3) = 4$, $-7 + 3 = -4$.

Try This

1. -3
2. -9
3. -4
4. 2
5. $4 + (-5)$
6. $3 + (-3)$
7. $4 + (-1)$
8. $2 + (-4)$

Hands-On Lab Recording Sheet 2-3
Think and Discuss

1. Show 5 red chips paired with yellow chips. Then take away the 5 yellow chips.
2. No. Each zero pair remaining equals zero.

3. No. $2 - 3$ can be modeled with 2 yellow chips plus one zero pair of a red chips and a yellow chip. Then 3 yellow chips are taken away, leaving 1 red chip. $3 - 2$ is modeled by taking 2 yellow chips from 3 yellow chips, leaving 1 yellow chip.
4. Sample answer: If two integers with the same sign are subtracted, subtract the unsigned numbers. If the first number has a larger unsigned value, the answer has the same sign as the first number. If not, the answer has the same sign as the number being subtracted: $3 - 2 = 1$; $2 - 3 = -1$; $-3 - (-2) = -1$; $-2 - (-3) = 1$; If two numbers with different signs are subtracted, add the unsigned numbers. The sign of the answer is the same as the sign of the first number: $3 - (-2) = 5$; $-2 - 3 = -5$; $2 - (-3) = 5$

Try This

1. 2
2. -2
3. 1
4. -1
5. -1
6. -3
7. 2
8. 2
9. 10

Hands-On Lab Recording Sheet 2-4
Activity 1
Think and Discuss

1. The sign is positive; the sign is negative; the sign is positive.
2. $1 \cdot 2$; $-1 \cdot (-12)$; $2 \cdot 6$; $-2 \cdot (-6)$; $3 \cdot 4$; $(-3) \cdot (-4)$

Try This

1. -20
2. -6
3. -6

Holt Mathematics

Answer Key

4. −10

5. Kathy spent $6.00.

Activity 2
Think and Discuss

1. The sign is a positive; the sign is a negative; the sign is a negative.

2. Both involve grouping numbers.

Try This

1. −3

2. −3

3. −4

4. −2

6. Each activity costs $6.00.

Hands-On Lab Recording Sheet 2-5
Think and Discuss

1. Subtraction, Addition.

2. Replace x with the solution: one side should equal the other side.

3. Subtracting a positive number is the same as adding the negative of that number.

Try This

1.

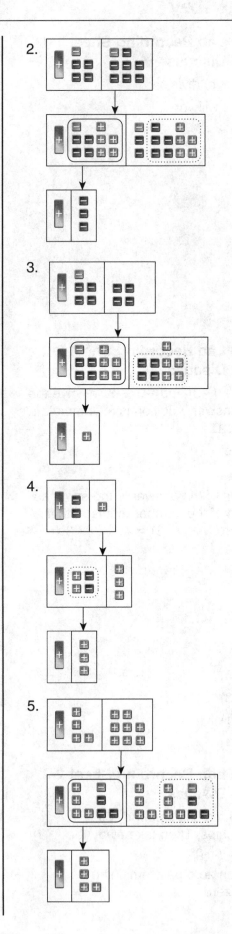

Holt Mathematics

Answer Key

6.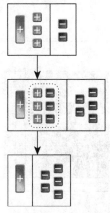

7.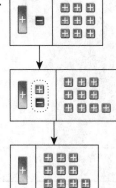

8.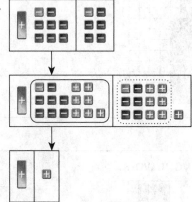

Hands-On Lab 2-6
Activity

1. Possible answer: A number is divisible by 2 if it ends in 0, 2, 4, 6, or 8. 84 and 50 are divisible by 2.

2. Possible answer: A number is divisible by 3 if the sum of its digits is divisible by 3. 75 and 240 are divisible by 3.

3. Possible answer: A number is divisible by 5 if it ends in 0 or 5. 95 and 120 are divisible by 5.

4. Possible answer: A number is divisible by 8 if the last three numbers form a number divisible by 8. 138 and 2,400 are divisible by 8.

5. Possible answer: A number is divisible by 9 if the sum of its digits is divisible by 9. 333 and 909 are divisible by 9.

Think and Discuss

1. Possible answer: Yes, since all even numbers end in 0, 2, 4, 6, or 8, all even numbers are divisible by 2.

2. Answer: No, the sum of the digits must be divisible by 3 for the number to be divisible by 3. The number 13 is not divisible by 3.

Try This

1. 64; 65

2. 96; 97

3. 124; 125

4. 105; 106

5. 144; 146

6. 408; 412

7. 765; 762

8. 110; 115

Possible answers:

9. 1,230

10. 1,245

11. 4,905

12. 2,916

13. 1,056

14. 396

Hands-On Lab 2-11
Activity

1.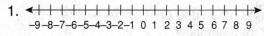

2.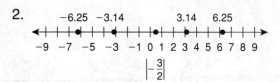

$$\left|-\frac{3}{2}\right|$$

4. −14.8 and 14.8

Holt Mathematics

Answer Key

Think and Discuss

1. Distance can never be negative.

2. True; a number and its opposites are the same distance from 0 on the number line, but on opposite sides of 0. For example, − 5 and 5 are both 5 units away from 0, but on opposite sides.

3. There are two points on the number line that are a distance of 14.8 units from 0.

Try This

1. 10.01

2. 7.14

3. $\sqrt{2}$

4. 6

5. 8.61

6. $\frac{6}{8}$

7. 2 or − 2

8. $\sqrt{5}$ or $-\sqrt{5}$

9. $6\frac{7}{12}$ or $-6\frac{7}{12}$

10. −4

Hands-On Lab Recording Sheet 3-3
Activity 1

1. a. 0.002

   b. 0.33

   c. 0.5

   d. 4.4

2. a. 1

   b. 0.88

   c. 1.05

   d. 0.72

Think and Discuss

1. You can use only whole blocks, not partial blocks.

Try This

1. 2

Show your work.

2. 0.08

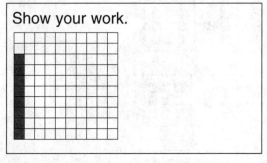

Show your work.

3. 0.48

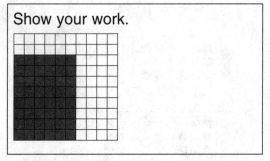

Show your work.

4. 0.615

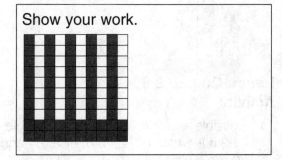

Show your work.

Holt Mathematics

Answer Key

5. 1.2

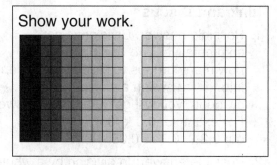

6. 0.99

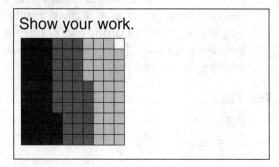

7. 1.25

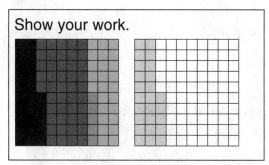

8. 1.26

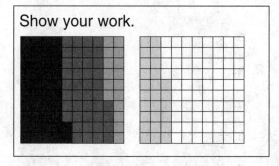

Activity 2

1. a. 0.12

   b. 0.01

   c. 0.04

   d. 0.02

Think and Discuss

1. First shade 5 rows one color, and then shade 5 columns a second color. The answer is the region that was shaded twice.

2. Shade the number of squares for the decimal as many times as the whole number.

Try This

1. 0.36

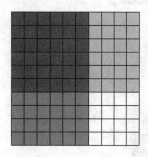

2. 0.2

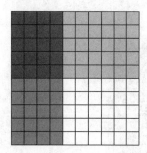

3. 0.24

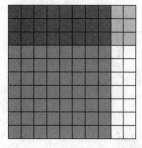

Holt Mathematics

Answer Key

4 0.16

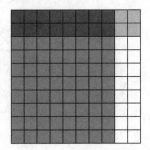

5. 0.9

6. 0.64

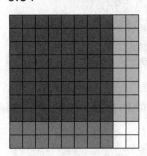

7. 1

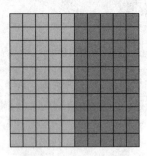

8. 0.09

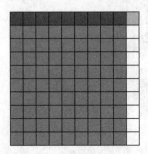

Hands-On Lab Recording Sheet 3-4
Think and Discuss

1. Possible answer: Division is not commutative. The divisor tells you how many groups to break the dividend into. If you switch a divisor and a dividend, you will get a different answer. For example, $0.8 \div 0.2 = 4$; but $0.2 \div 0.8 = 0.25$

2. Possible answer: In division by a whole number, the divisor tells you how many groups to separate the dividend into. In division by a decimal, the divisor tells you the size of the groups to separate the dividend into. The quotient is how many groups you have.

Try This

1. 0.2
2. 0.15
3. 3
4. 1.5
5. 0.5
6. 0.45
7. 3
8. 2

Hands-On Lab Recording Sheet 3-8

1. a. $\frac{2}{3}$

   b. $\frac{3}{4}$

   c. $\frac{5}{12}$

   d. $\frac{3}{5}$

2. a. $\frac{5}{6}$

   b. $\frac{3}{4}$

   c. $\frac{1}{2}$

   d. $\frac{5}{12}$

3. a. $1\frac{1}{2}$

   b. $1\frac{1}{6}$

Holt Mathematics

Answer Key

c. $1\frac{1}{12}$

d. $1\frac{1}{8}$

4. a. $\frac{1}{3}$

b. $\frac{1}{12}$

c. $\frac{1}{6}$

d. $\frac{1}{12}$

Think and Discuss

1.

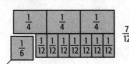

Possible answer: Model $\frac{3}{4}$. Place a $\frac{1}{6}$ bar beneath bars that show $\frac{3}{4}$, and find which fraction fills the remaining space. The fraction that fits is $\frac{7}{12}$.

2.

3.

Try This

1. 1

2. $\frac{5}{6}$

3. $\frac{5}{12}$

4. $\frac{11}{12}$

5. $\frac{1}{12}$

6. $\frac{1}{4}$

7. $\frac{7}{12}$

8. $\frac{5}{12}$

9. $\frac{7}{8}$ pizza

10. $\frac{1}{12}$ mile

Hands-On Lab Recording Sheet 3-10
Activity 1
Think and Discuss

1. Possible answer: Yes, multiplication is commutative, so both models will have the same parts shaded. The only difference in the models will be the orientation, or placement, of the shaded parts.

2. Possible answer: Suppose you have 2 fraction factors: factor A, $\frac{2}{3}$, and factor B, $\frac{1}{5}$. The product is less than factor B because a part of a part must be less than the original part. The product is less than factor A because you are finding $\frac{2}{3}$ of a part, rather than $\frac{2}{3}$ of a whole.

Try This

1. $\frac{1}{4}$

2. $\frac{1}{2}$

3. $\frac{5}{24}$

4. $\frac{1}{3}$

Activity 2
Think and Discuss

1. Possible answer: No, division is not commutative. The 2 models will show different groupings and different quotients.

2. Possible answer: The quotient is greater than the dividend. You are finding how many fractional parts are in the whole, or the dividend.

Try This

1. $\frac{7}{2}$ or $3\frac{1}{2}$

2. $\frac{8}{3}$ or $2\frac{2}{3}$

3. $\frac{3}{2}$ or $1\frac{1}{2}$

Holt Mathematics

Answer Key

4. $\frac{17}{3}$ or $5\frac{2}{3}$

Hands-On Lab 3-10
Activity

1. a.

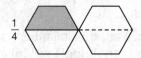

b.

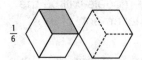

c.

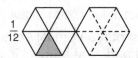

d.

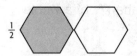

e.

$\frac{2}{6} = \frac{1}{3}$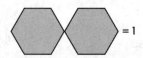

2. a. 1;

b. $\frac{1}{3}$;

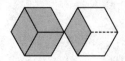

c. $\frac{2}{3}$;

d. $\frac{6}{12} = \frac{1}{2}$;

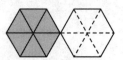

3. a.

b.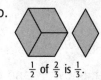

$\frac{1}{2}$ of $\frac{2}{3}$ is $\frac{1}{3}$.

c.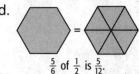

$\frac{1}{3}$ of $\frac{1}{2}$ is $\frac{1}{6}$.

d.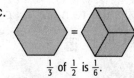

$\frac{5}{6}$ of $\frac{1}{2}$ is $\frac{5}{12}$.

4. a.

 It takes 2 pattern blocks representing $\frac{1}{6}$ to cover $\frac{1}{3}$ exactly.

b.

 It takes 6 pattern blocks representing $\frac{1}{12}$ to cover $\frac{1}{2}$ exactly.

c.

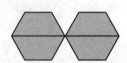

d.

 It takes 3 pattern blocks representing $\frac{1}{6}$ to cover $\frac{1}{2}$ exactly.

Holt Mathematics

Answer Key

Think and Discuss

1. No, the order of the factors differs so the models differ.

2. $\frac{1}{2}$; $\frac{1}{6}$; $\frac{1}{3}$

3. $\frac{1}{12}$; $\frac{1}{6}$; $\frac{1}{4}$; $\frac{1}{3}$; $\frac{1}{2}$; Fractions with lesser denominators represent greater numbers.

Try This

1.

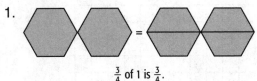

$\frac{3}{4}$ of 1 is $\frac{3}{4}$.

2.

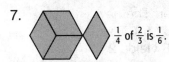 $\frac{1}{2}$ of $\frac{1}{6}$ is $\frac{1}{12}$.

3. It takes 1 pattern block representing $\frac{1}{2}$ to cover $\frac{1}{2}$ exactly.

4. $\frac{2}{3}$ of $\frac{3}{6}$ is $\frac{2}{6}$, or $\frac{1}{3}$.

5.

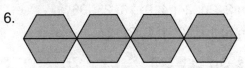 $\frac{3}{4}$ of $\frac{1}{3}$ is $\frac{3}{12}$, or $\frac{1}{4}$.

6.

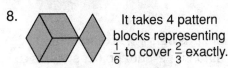

It takes 8 pattern blocks

7. $\frac{1}{4}$ of $\frac{2}{3}$ is $\frac{1}{6}$.

8. It takes 4 pattern blocks representing $\frac{1}{6}$ to cover $\frac{2}{3}$ exactly.

9. $\frac{1}{6}$ hour

Hands-On Lab 3-11
Think and Discuss

1. Write each number as the product of

expressions with exponents and bases that are prime numbers. Then rewrite the division as the product of the first number times the reciprocal of the divisor.

2. $\frac{2^3}{2^4} = \frac{222}{2222}$, which is equal to $\frac{2}{2} \cdot \frac{2}{2} \cdot \frac{2}{2} \cdot \frac{2}{2}$, or $1 \cdot 1 \cdot 1 \cdot \frac{1}{2}$. The numerator has the greatest exponent. So, $\frac{2^3}{2^4} = \frac{1}{2^{4-3}}$.

Try This

1. $\frac{2}{3}$

2. $\frac{3}{2}$ or $1\frac{1}{2}$

3. $\frac{22}{9}$ or $2\frac{4}{9}$

4. $\frac{4}{25}$

5. 30

6. $\frac{5}{6}$

7. $\frac{14}{9}$ or $1\frac{5}{9}$

8. $\frac{14}{9}$ or $1\frac{5}{9}$

9. $\frac{1}{6}$

10. $\frac{5}{4}$ or $1\frac{1}{4}$

11. $\frac{15}{16}$

12. $\frac{5}{4}$ or $1\frac{1}{4}$

13. $\frac{2}{3}$

14. 2

15. $\frac{25}{11}$ or $2\frac{3}{11}$

16. 3

Hands-On Lab 4-3
Activity

1. only one

2. For most balls, the ratio will be about the same.

3. For most balls, $b = 0.8 \times d$.

Holt Mathematics

Answer Key

Think and Discuss

1. 110; 165; 220; 275
2. 60; 70; 80; 90; 100

Try This

1. 255 m
2. $d = 17t$
3. a. yes

   b. no

   c. yes

Hands-On Lab 4-4
Activity

10; 13; The graph and the table both show that everytime X increases by 1, Y increases by 3.

Think and Discuss

1. a. y would increase by 300.

   b. y would decrease by 150.
2. If x decreased by 20, y would decrease by 60.

Try This

1. a. $y = -5x$

   b. In a week the watch will lose 35 minutes, or −35.
2.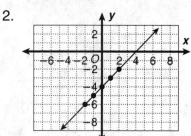

   b. The value of y increases by 4 when x increases by 4.
3. The value of y is multiplied by 4.

Hands-On Recording Sheet 4-6
Think and Discuss

1. The difference between consecutive y-values, corresponding to consecutive x-values, is constant.
2. No. The difference between consecutive

y-values is not constant. Or, the graph is not a straight line.

Try This

2.

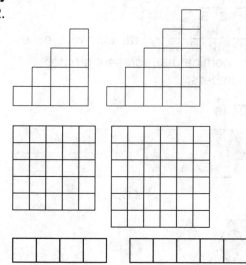

4.

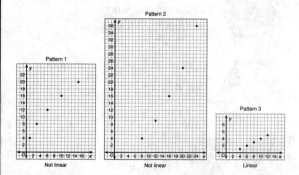

Pattern 1: 1; 3; 6; 10; 15; 16; 20

Pattern 2: 20; 24; 4; 9; 16; 25; 36

Pattern 3: 10; 12; 1; 2; 3; 4; 5

Hands-On Lab 5-3
Think and Discuss

1. Possible answer: The new proportion is 36 : 54. Dividing each side by 18 yields 2 : 3.

Try This

1. Possible answer: For example, cutting each strip into 2 equal pieces yields a proportion 2 : 8. Cutting each 2 into three pieces and each 8 into four pieces yields a proportion 6 : 32. This proportion can be converted to 1 : 4 by reversing the math of the previous step: (6 • 4) : (32 • 3).

Holt Mathematics

Answer Key

Hands-On Lab Recording Sheet 5-6
Think and Discuss

1. Possible answer: The number of picas is 6 times the number of inches.

2. $p = 6n$

3. 61

Try This

1. line

2. 36 picas

3. 9 in.

4. 6 in. by 5 in.

Hands-On Lab 5-7
Think and Discuss

1. There are various ways to make the triangle similar. One of the simplest is to cut the vertical leg from 10 squares to 9 squares, draw a line from the vertical endpoint to the horizontal endpoint and cut a new hypotenuse. The vertical and horizontal sides are now in a 3 : 4 ratio like the original.

2. Because all circles are similar. Any circle can be expressed as a ratio of any other circle.

Try This

1. This activity works with virtually all figures except circles. Figures with regular and corresponding sides, such as rectangles, are easier to modify than odd-shaped figures such as trapezoids, and figures with fewer sides and angles are easier than those with many sides.

Hands-On Lab 5-7A
Activity

2; 8

$\frac{8}{2} = \frac{4}{1}$

6 in^2; 54 in^2; $\frac{3}{1}$; $\frac{54}{6} = \frac{9}{1}$; 10 m^2; 22.5 m^2; $\frac{3}{2}$;

$\frac{22.5}{10} = \frac{9}{4}$

Think and Discuss

1. The ratio of the areas equals the ratio of the sides.

2. Both the base and the height are multiplied by $\frac{10}{3}$. The area of a rectangle is bh. Therefore, the ratio of the areas is

$\frac{10}{3} \times \frac{10}{3} = \frac{100}{9}$.

3. $\frac{6}{1}$

Try This

1. $\frac{1}{2} \cdot 1 \cdot 2 = 1$; $\frac{1}{2} \cdot 3 \cdot 6 = 9$

1 square unit; 9 square units; $\frac{3}{1}$; $\frac{9}{1}$

2. 2 in^2; 8 in^2; $\frac{2}{1}$; $\frac{8}{2} = \frac{4}{1}$; 12 ft^2; 27 ft^2;

$\frac{3}{2}$; $\frac{27}{12} = \frac{9}{4}$

3. The relationships are the same: the ratios of the areas of both triangles and rectangles is the square of their corresponding sides.

Hands-On Lab 5-8
Think and Discuss

1. The new dimensions would be 17 feet by 22 feet.

Try This

1. Students' answers should resemble the drawing on page 60. Be sure they have drawn all items at the same scale of 3 : 1.

Hands-On Lab 5-8A
Activity

$\frac{1}{120}$; $\frac{x}{5} = \frac{1}{120}$; $120x = 5$; $x = \frac{5}{120} = \frac{1}{24}$;

Since 1 yard is 36 inches, $\frac{1}{24}$ year equals

$\frac{1}{24} \cdot 36$, or 1.5 inches.

Think and Discuss

1. The field and the model are similar figures. In similar figures corresponding angles have the same measurement.

2. The comparison would be distorted if you used different units of measurement.

Try This

1. 10 yd

2. 10 feet; 20 feet

4. Answers will vary.

Holt Mathematics

Answer Key

Hands-On Lab 6-1
Think and Discuss

1. Step 1: Multiply the fraction by 100.

$$\frac{7}{33} \times \frac{100}{1} = \frac{700}{33} = 21.\overline{21} \text{ or } 21.2\%$$

Try This

1. $\frac{3}{20}$

2. 62.5%

3. 9

Hands-On Lab Recording Sheet 6-4
Activity 1
Think and Discuss

1. To model 36.75%, fill in 36 squares out of 100, plus $\frac{3}{4}$ of one additional square. Model 0.7% by filling in seven-tenths of one square.

Try This

1.

2.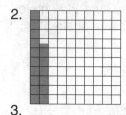

3.

4.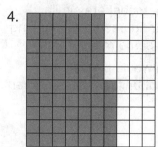

5.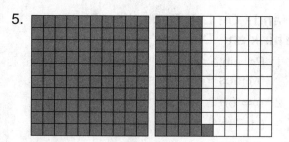

Activity 2
Think and Discuss

1. Draw a percent bar of 10 equal segments. Label the divisions from 0% to 100%. Draw a quantity bar of the same length underneath; label the endpoints 0 and the number (x). Divide the quantity bar into eighths. Label the corresponding quantities from $\frac{1}{8}x$ to $\frac{7}{8}x$. Look at the percent bar for the percent you wish to find and estimate what quantity lies under it on the quantity bar.

2. Reading the percent bar and the quantity bar required making a judgment by eye as to where numbers fall between the indicated intervals.

Try This

1.

	0 10 20 30 40 50 60 70 80 90 100%
Percent bar	

	0 3.6 7.2 10.8 14.4 18 21.6 25.2 28.8 32.4 36
Quantity bar	

2.

	0 10 20 30 40 50 60 70 80 90 100%
Percent bar	

	0 1.5 3 4.5 6 7.5 9 10.5 12 13.5 15
Quantity bar	

3.

	0 10 20 30 40 50 60 70 80 90 100 110 120 130 140%
Percent bar	

	0 4 8 12 16 20 24 28 32 36 44 44 48 52 56
Quantity bar	

Holt Mathematics

Answer Key

4.

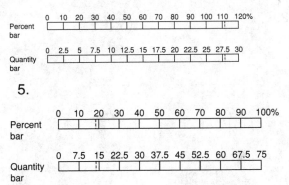

5.

Hands-On Lab 6-5
Think and Discuss

1. To decrease the area of the square by 25%, one-fourth of its area must be removed. So, dividing the square into 4 parts makes it easy to remove one-fourth of the square.

2. 75%

3. a 1-by-5 rectangle since 40% is equivalent to $\frac{2}{5}$

4. 4 : 3, $33\frac{1}{3}$%; this means the new rectangle is 100% plus a additional $33\frac{1}{3}$% of the size of the original square.

Try This

1.

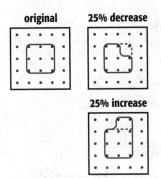

2.

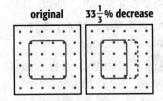

3.

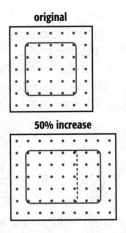

4.

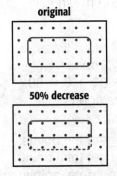

5. A 1-by-10 rectangle; increasing a 1-by-10 rectangle by 10% means adding one-tenth, which is equivalent to one square.

6. 100%

Hands-On Lab 7-1
Activity

42.7%; 3.2%; 54.1%; 100%

Think and Discuss

1. Cumulative frequency is a running total. Relative frequency compares the frequency of a group to the total of the frequencies of all groups.

2. The sum must be 100% because each group is part of a whole. The relative frequency is the percent that each part is of the whole. The whole is 100%.

Try This

1. 1.7%; 0%; 7.5%; 5.2%; 2.2%; 3.2%; 14.5%; 6.7%; 22.2%; 36.7%; 99.9%

2. 100%

Holt Mathematics

Answer Key

Hands-On Lab 7-2
Think and Discuss

1. If the score that is weighted is greater than the other scores, the weighted average will be greater. If the score that is weighted is less than the other scores, the weighted average will be less.

Try This

1. a. 78

2. weighted average: 91; 95; 86; 84 mean: 93.75; 93.75; 87.5; 82.5

3. If the score that is weighted is less than the other scores, the weighted average will be greater than the mean.

4. a. 8; 30; 4

   b. Enter "4" a total of three times; enter "30" twice; enter "8" once.
   4 + 4 + 4 + 30 + 30 + 8 = 80.
   80 ÷ 6 = 13.3 average points per game.

   c. Multiply 8 by 1 to get total points; multiply 30 by 2 to get total points; multiply 4 by 3 to get total points; add up the total points and divide by 6.

Hands-On Lab 7-3

The difference between April (26 inches) and January (8 inches) is 18 inches.

Possible answer: The graph demonstrates visually the increase in rainfall from January to April and the decline thereafter.

Think and Discuss

1. Possible answer: Line graphs, histograms, and stem-and-leaf plots would also be useful for representing this information. A circle graph would not represent this information effectively.

2. Possible answer: The bar graph provides a strong visual representation of each month's rainfall compared to each other month.

Try This

2.

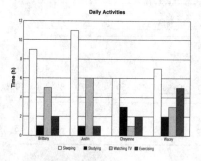

Hands-On Lab 7-5
Activity 1
Think and Discuss

1. They represent all of the people who play team sports and all of the people who play an instrument.

2. Three circles would overlap to show three data sets. The Venn diagram would have four overlapping areas.

Try This

1. 36

2. 16

3. 39

4.

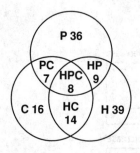

Activity 2
Think and Discuss

1. There will be 4 individual sets of data and 9 overlapping areas in the movie data in a Venn diagram of 4 data sets.

2. A Venn diagram of student ages might be simply a row of circles.

   14 **15** **16** **17** There would be no overlap, because one does not turn officially the next higher age until the date of birth.

Try This

Holt Mathematics

Answer Key

1. Check students' work.

2. a. 33

   b. 12

   c. 7

Hands-On Lab 7-8
Think and Discuss

1. Possible answer: The variables shoe size and last two digits of phone number do not appear to form a pattern. There is no relationship between shoe size and the last two digits of phone numbers.

2. Possible answer: There was no pattern.

3. Possible answer: No; the points are not in a line.

Try This

1.

The points on the graph appear to cluster around a straight line slanting up from left to right.

Hands-On Lab 7-9
Activity

1. A circle graph shows the parts of the whole. Here the data do not form any sort of complete total together, so the circle graph does not make sense. A line graph would be more appropriate.

2. A line graph is most suitable for showing changes over time. Here there is no time element. The data items consist of the entire club budget—just the sort of data that should be displayed in a circle graph.

Think and Discuss

1. a. A bar chart compares the smaller and larger numbers with each other. The circle graph compares each data item to some larger whole of which the data item is a part.

   b. A line plot shows items that fall into distinct and mutually exclusive categories. A Venn diagram is most useful to describe a situation where some data items fall into two categories at once.

2. In most cases, you would see no error message. Choosing the right kind of graph requires a judgment that is made by you, not the computer.

Try This

1. Answers will vary.

Hands-On Lab 8-1
Think and Discuss

1. yes

2. yes

3. two

4. three

Try This

1. Check students' drawings. Possible answer:

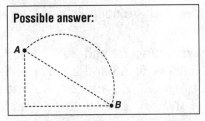

2. The shortest distance between two points will always be a straight line.

Hands-On Lab 8-2
Think and Discuss

1. Yes; you can use the protractor to find the measurements of the rays that make up the angle. The measurements can then be subtracted to find the actual measurement of the angle.

Try This

1. 120°, obtuse

2. 90°, right

3. 85°, acute

Holt Mathematics

Answer Key

Hands-On Lab Recording Sheet 8-2
Activity 1
Think and Discuss

1. subtract the measure of ∠*AVB* from the measure of ∠*AVC*.

Try This

1. 90°
2. 25°
3. 90°

Activity 2
Think and Discuss

1. If an angle pair is complementary, the sum of their measures is 90°. If an angle pair is supplementary, the sum of their measures is 180°.

Try This

1. 80°, 10°, complementary
2. 40°, 140°, supplementary
3. 53°, 29°, neither
4. 95°, 85°, supplementary
5. The sides that are not adjacent form a straight line.
6. Complementary: ∠1 and ∠2; ∠3 and ∠4; ∠5 and ∠6; ∠8 and ∠7; ∠1 and ∠5; ∠1 and ∠3; ∠1 and ∠7; ∠2 and ∠4; ∠2 and ∠5; ∠2 and ∠8; ∠3 and ∠5; ∠3 and ∠8; ∠4 and ∠6; ∠4 and ∠7; ∠5 and ∠7; ∠6 and ∠8
Supplementary: ∠12 and ∠9; ∠9 and ∠10; ∠10 and ∠11; ∠11 and ∠12.

Hands-On Lab Recording Sheet 8-3
Think and Discuss

1. 3 bisectors
2. 22°

Try This

1.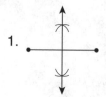

2.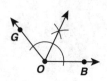

3.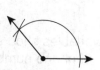

Hands-On Lab 8-3
Activity 1

Activity 2

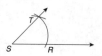

Activity 3

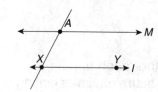

Activity 4

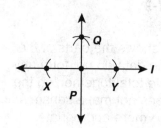

Activity 5

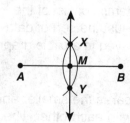

Holt Mathematics

Answer Key

Activity 6

Try This

Check students' work.

Hands-On Lab 8-3A
Activity

1. 55°; 125°; 125°; 55°; 55°; 125°; 125°; 55°

2. a. interior angles: 3, 4, 5, and 6

   b. exterior angles: 1, 2, 7, and 8

Think and Discuss

1. Possible answer: The interior angles are 3, 4, 5, and 6. The exterior angles are 1, 2, 7, and 8. The alternate interior angles are 3 and 6, 4 and 5. The alternate exterior angles are 1 and 8, 2 and 7.

2. 55°, 125°, 55°, 55°, 125°, 125°, 55°

Try This

1. Possible answer: Angle 1 measures 125°. Angles 2, 3, 6, and 7 each have a measure of 55°, since a 55° angle is supplementary to a 125° angle. Angles 4, 5, and 8 each have a measure of 125°.

Hands-On-Lab 8-3B
Activity

1. They appear to be perpendicular, so they make a 90° angle.

2. They appear to be parallel.

Think and Discuss

1. Possible answers: Measure one of the angles formed by the intersection of *NO* and *PH*. If the angle is 90° , the lines are perpendicular.

2. If *ST* is perpendicular to *LR*, then angle *USW* is a right angle.

Try This

1.

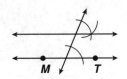

2.

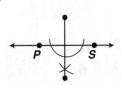

Hands-On Lab Recording Sheet 8-4
Think and Discuss

1. the sum of the percents is 100; the sum of the decimals is 1; the sum of the fractions is 1; the sum of the degrees is 360.

2. Sample answer: Data that are parts of a whole.

3. Sample answer: the measure of each section is that percent, decimal, or fraction of 180°.

Try This

1. Reading: 0.3; $\frac{3}{10}$; 108; Playing Sports: 0.25; $\frac{1}{4}$; 90; Working on Computer: 0.4; $\frac{2}{5}$; 144; Watching TV: 0.05; $\frac{1}{20}$; 18

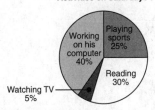

Hands-On Lab 8-5
Think and Discuss

1. Line segments allow you to draw polygons, because they have straight sides. A circle could not be drawn using this method because it has a curved side.

Holt Mathematics

Answer Key

Try This

1.

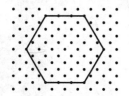

2.

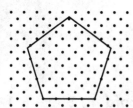

3.

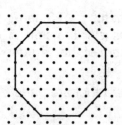

4.

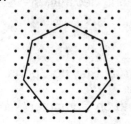

5.

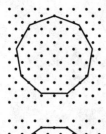

6.

Hands-On Lab 8-5A
Activity

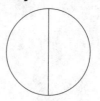

Think and Discuss

1. Yes, the sides of an equilateral triangle are congruent.

2. No; when bisecting the diameter of a circle, you must use a compass opening that is greater than the radius of a circle, however you must use a compass opening equal to the radius of the circle.

Holt Mathematics

Answer Key

3. They were all constructed using the same opening on the compass; the radius of the circle and the sides of the hexagon have the same measure.

4. No; each side of a square inscribed in a circle is equal in length to the compass opening used to construct the perpendicular bisector of the diameter, which must be greater than the radius of the circle.

Try This

1.

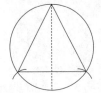

2.

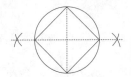

3.

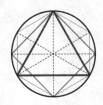

4.

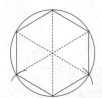

Hands-On Lab 8-5B
Activity

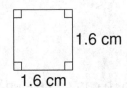

1.6 cm

1.6 cm

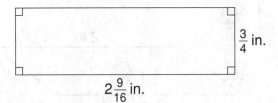

$\frac{3}{4}$ in.

$2\frac{9}{16}$ in.

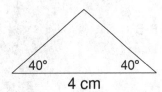

40°   40°

4 cm

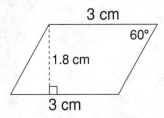

3 cm

60°

1.8 cm

3 cm

Think and Discuss

1. Before you can draw anything, you need to know the shape. Without the dimensions, you would not know how big to make the figure.

2. You can use one of the lines on the paper. This second line will be a distance of the height of the parallelogram from the first time.

Try This

1.

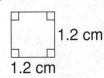

1.2 cm

1.2 cm

2.

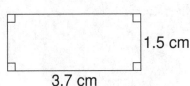

1.5 cm

3.7 cm

3.

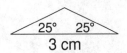

25°   25°

3 cm

Holt Mathematics

Answer Key

4.

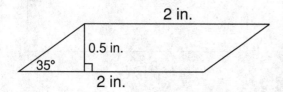

Hands-On Lab 8-6
Activity

1.

2. Each is 3 cm long.

3. Each is 60°.

Think and Discuss

1. The compass opening was set to 3 cm to construct the sides.

2. Use the same construction as for an equilateral triangle. Equilateral triangles have 3 congruent angles.

Try This

1.

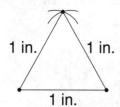

2.

Hands-On Lab 8-8
Activity

1.

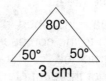

This is an isosceles triangle.

2.

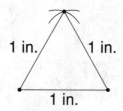

It is a trapezoid.

3.

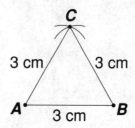

It is a rhombus.

Think and Discuss

1. The figure is now a rectangle.

Try This

1.

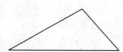

This is a square.

2.

Both clue a and clue b can be deleted. It is an equilateral triangle.

Holt Mathematics

Answer Key

Hands-On Lab 8-9
Activity

1. No; Yes because their angles are congruent; The sides are proportional: $\frac{3}{6} = \frac{4}{8} = \frac{5}{10}$;

2. The triangles are similar because their sides are proportional.

Think and Discuss

1. I agree. If two angles of one triangle are specified, there is only one angle measure possible for the third angle.

Try This

1. Yes because the angles are congruent. They are also similar because the sides are proportional.

2. Yes, because the two given sides are proportional and the included angles are congruent. They are also similar because the three sides are proportional.

Hands-On Lab 8-10
Activity

1. Each segment of the image is two times the length of the original.

Think and Discuss

1. Examples will vary. Some examples are translations: repeating borders, wallpaper patterns, fabrics, reflections: all figures with line symmetry, mirror images; rotations: many corporate logos, the recycle symbol; dilations: photo enlargements, scale models.

Try This

1. a.

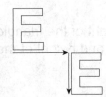

b.

c.

Hands-On Lab Recording Sheet 8-11
Think and Discuss

1. Transformation tessellations are translated images to create a pattern, and rotation tessellations use rotated images to create a pattern.

Try This

1. Check students' work.

2. Check students' work.

Hands-On Lab 8-11
Think and Discuss

1. Possible answer: Yes, because the fold is your line of symmetry. As long as you make one of the sides part of the fold, any regular shape you cut out will be symmetrical.

Try This

1. Possible answer: As long as the shape you start with is symmetrical, then two symmetrical shapes will be created when you cut them out of the folded paper, but if the folded paper does not make symmetrical figures, then the figure you cut out will not be symmetrical either.

Hands-On Lab 9-1
Think and Discuss

1. 164 quarters

2. A graduated cylinder is more precise than a measuring cup because the unit of measurement is smaller.

Holt Mathematics

Answer Key

Try This

1. 1 cup

2. 500 gallons

3. about 4.5 cups of water will fill a one-liter beaker; = 4.5 c

4. about 460 milliliters of water are needed to fill a 2 cup container; 2 c = 460 ml

5. −23. Check students' work.

Hands-On Lab 9-1A
Activity 1
Think and Discuss

1. 18.1 cm; the measurement to the nearest tenth best represents the actual length because it gives more exact information about the length of the pencil.

2. No; the measurement to the nearest tenth of a centimeter is more exact than a measurement in inches because the centimeter is a smaller unit than the inch.

Try This

1. 3 cm; 3.2 cm

2. 2 cm; 1.6 cm

Activity 2
Think and Discuss

1. 2.9 cm; 8.9 cm; 1 inch is about 2.5 cm

Try This

1. length: $\frac{3}{4}$ in.; width: $\frac{3}{4}$ in.; perimeter: 3 in.

2. length: $\frac{1}{4}$ in.; width: $2\frac{3}{4}$ in.; perimeter: 6 in.

3. length: $\frac{7}{8}$ in., width: $2\frac{1}{4}$ in.; perimeter: $6\frac{1}{4}$ in.

4. length: $\frac{1}{2}$ in.; width: $2\frac{3}{8}$ in.; perimeter: $5\frac{3}{4}$ in.

Hands-On Lab Recording Sheet 9-2
Activity 1
Think and Discuss

1. The point lies on a straight line.

2. For each rectangle, the sum of the length and the width is $\frac{1}{2}$ the perimeter.

3. $P = 2(+w)$ or $P = 2 + 2w$

Try This

1. 20 in

2. 24 ft

3. 20 cm

Activity 2
Think and Discuss

1. The points are close to lying on a straight line.

2. Possible answer: $\pi = 3.14$

Try This

1. $C = \pi d$

2. Possible answer: $C = 12.56$ cm

Hands-On Lab Recording Sheet 9-3
Activity 1
Think and Discuss

1. The length and width of the rectangle are equal to the base and height of the parallelogram.

2. $A = bh$

Try This

1. The formula works for any parallelogram; $A = 5 \cdot 3 = 15$ in^2

2. They all have the same area.

Activity 2
Think and Discuss

1. The base and height of the triangle are equal to the base and height of the parallelogram.

2. $A = \frac{1}{2}bh$

Try This

1. 25 ft^2

Holt Mathematics

Answer Key

Activity 3

1. length of base: $b^1 + b^2$; area of parallelogram: $h(b^1 + b^2)$
2. $\frac{1}{2}h(b^1 + b^2)$
3. 40 in^2

Hands-On Lab 9-3
Think and Discuss

1. The formula for the area of a rectangle $A = h \cdot \ell$ also applies to the area of a parallelogram, but h is a vertical height and not the length of the left and right sides.

Try This

1. $A = b \cdot \ell = 9 \cdot 15 = 135$ cm^2

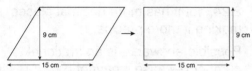

2. $A = b \cdot \ell = 7 \cdot 3 = 21$ cm^2

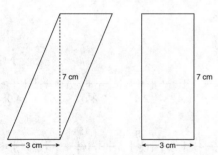

Hands-On Lab 9-4
Think and Discuss

1. Trapezoid 1 and Trapezoid 2 have the same area:

   $A_{T1} = \frac{5}{2}(9 + 4.5) = 3375$ cm^2; $A_{T2} = \frac{5}{2}(12 + 1.5) = 33.75$ cm^2

   They have the same area, because they have the same height (5 cm) and the sum of their lengths (13.5 cm) is the same.

Try This

1. The area of the parallelogram
   $A_p = h \cdot b = 10 \cdot 4 = 40$ cm^2

The area of each triangle is $A_T = \frac{h}{2} \cdot b = \frac{10}{2} \cdot 4 = 20$ cm^2

2. The area of the parallelogram
   $A_p = h(a + b) = 2(6 + 4) = 20$ cm^2

   The area of the trapezoid is
   $A_{TZ} = \frac{h}{2}(a + b) = \frac{2}{2}(6 + 4) = 10$ cm^2

Hands-On Lab 9-4A
Think and Discuss

1. No, you would need at least one other measurement, because there might be more than one combination of base and height that would have been the same area.

Try This

1. 4 in.
2. 180 cm^2
3. 8.5 in.
4. 16 ft

Hands-On Lab Recording Sheet 9-7
Activity 1
Think and Discuss

1. The square root, multiplied by itself, equals the total number of small squares.

2. The square root is equal to the number of small squares on a side of the figure.

Try This

1. 11
2. 12
3. 14

Activity 2
Think and Discuss

1. If x is the non-perfect square, find the largest perfect square that is less than x and the smallest perfect square that is greater than x. Then $\sqrt{x}$ lies between the square roots of those two perfect squares.

Holt Mathematics

Answer Key

2. A 4 × 4 square contains 16 small squares. A 5 × 5 square contains 25 small squares. Since 16 < 19 < 25, $4 < \sqrt{19} < 5$.

3. Any number greater than 25 and less than 36.

Try This

1. 4.4
2. 3.2
3. 5.3
4. 5.9

Hands-On Lab Recording Sheet 9-8
Activity 1
Think and Discuss

1. The area of the two red squares added together is equal to the area of the blue square.

2. a. Squaring the side length of a square will give you the area of a square.

   b. Squaring the lengths of each side of the triangle will give you the area of the square that shares one of its sides.

   c. $a^2 + b^2 = c^2$

Try This

1. Yes; the relationship is true for each isosceles triangle.

Activity 2

1. 9, 16, 25; If you add the areas of the two smaller squares, you get the area of the largest square.

2. 5

3. $3^2 + 4^2 = 5^2$; 9 + 16 = 25; the equation seems to be true for right triangles other than just isosceles right triangles.

4. No; for example, the relationship is not true for an equilateral triangle with side length 1. $1^2 + 1^2 \neq 1^2$

Try This

1. No; the total area of the red squares is 25, but the area of the blue square is 36.

2. Yes; to find the length of the longest side, square each of the smaller sides and add them together: $9^2 + 12^2 =$ 81 + 144 = 225. The length of the longest sides is the square root of 225: $\sqrt{225} = 15$.

3. Square both numbers. Subtract the square of the shorter side from the square of the longest side. The length of the third side is the square root of the difference.

Hands-On Lab 9-ext
Think and Discuss

1. Possible answer: $\sqrt{5} = 2.23606\ldots$; This answer is similar to the one found in the activity since it is between 2.23 and 2.24, but it has more decimal places, making it more precise.

2. Possible answer: π is an irrational number because it cannot be expressed as a terminating or repeating decimal.

Try This

1.

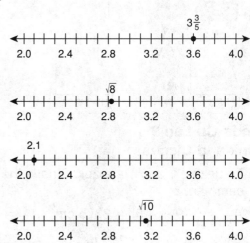

2.

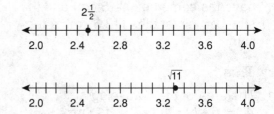

Answer Key

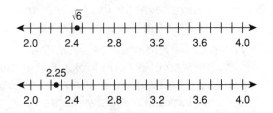

2.0 2.4 2.8 3.2 3.6 4.0

Hands-On Lab Recording Sheet 10-1
Activity 1
Think and Discuss

1. 15

2. Add a cube on top of any cube on top of the figure.

3. You could remove any cube.

Try This

1.

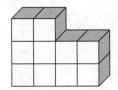

2.

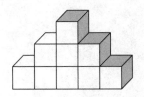

3.

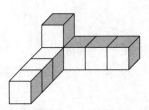

4.

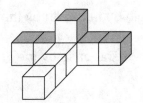

Activity 2
Think and Discuss

1. Yes, you can start with any view (front, top, or side), then add cubes so the figure matches one of the 2 remaining views, then take away cubes using whichever view you haven't used to build the figure.

Try This

1.

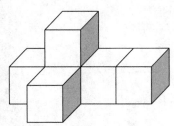

2.

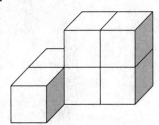

3. figure D

Hands-On Lab 10-1
Activity

1.

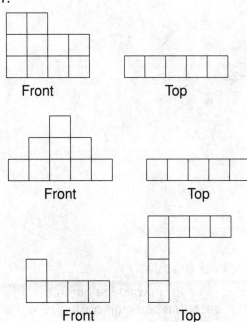

Front   Top

Front   Top

Front   Top

Holt Mathematics

Answer Key

2.

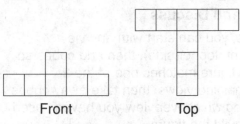

Front   Top

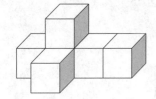

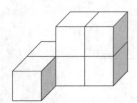

3.

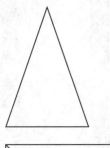

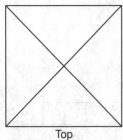

Top

Side

Think and Discuss

1. You have to draw line segments from the base to a common point above the base.

2. You draw an oval for the base of the cone and for the base of a hemisphere.

3. When drawn from a side view, the circular base of a cone looks like an oval and the rectangle base of a rectangular pyramid looks like a parallelogram.

Try This

1.

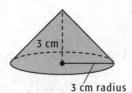

3 cm

3 cm radius

2.

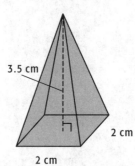

3.5 cm

2 cm

2 cm

3.

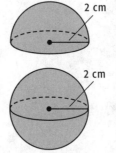

2 cm

2 cm

Hands-On Lab Recording Sheet 10-2
Activity 1
Think and Discuss

1. multiply the length by the width by the weight.

2. multiply the area of the base by the height.

3. $V = Bh$

Try This

1. 72 cm^3

2. 42 cm^3

Holt Mathematics

Answer Key

3. 24 cm^3

Activity 2
Think and Discuss

1. multiply the area of the base by the height.

2. $V = Bh$

3. The area of the base equals the area of the circle: $V = \pi r^2 h$

Try This

1. 12.6 cm^3

2. 56.5 cm^3

4. 31.4 cm^3

Hands-On Lab 10-2
Think and Discuss

1. Yes, the volume of a prism is 5 × 3 × 8 = 120 cubic inches. If the length were doubled to 10 inches, the volume would be 10 × 3 × 8 = 240 cubic inches, which is twice the volume of the original prism.

Try This

1. 10.5 in^3

Hands-On Lab 10-2A
Activity

1.

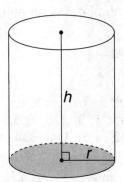

Think and Discuss

1. Possible Answer: It is about the same. Since the base of the prism is a rectangle, then $B = lw$

Step 1 : $V = (lw) \times h$

Step 2 : $V = (12)(4)(3)$

Step 3 : $V = 144$ in^3

Try This

1. Volume equals pi times radius squared times height.

2. Volume equals length times width times height.

3. 0.125 in^3

4. 21.195 ml

Hands-On Lab Recording Sheet 10-4
Think and Discuss

1. Answers will vary, depending upon the number of squares per inch.

2. Answers will vary, depend upon the number of squares per inch.

Try This

1.

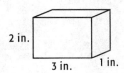

2.

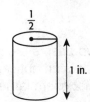

Hands-On Lab 10-4
Think and Discuss

1. $S_{cyl} = 2\pi r^2 + C \times h = 2\pi^2 + 2\pi rh$
   $= 2\pi r(r + h)$

Try This

1. $l = C = 2\pi r = 6.28$ cm; $S_{cyl} = 2\pi +$ 6.28
   $= 6.28 + 6.28 + 6.28 = 69.08^2$

Hands-On Lab Recording Sheet 10-5
Activity 1
Think and Discuss

1. Because each of these faces has a matching face: back, bottom, and "either side" face.

Holt Mathematics

Answer Key

2. Length is 5 cm, width is 3 cm, and height is 4 cm. The surface area is 94 cm^2.

Try This

1. 32 cm^2
2. 52 cm^2
3. 80 cm^2

Activity 2

1. The surface area of B is four times the the surface area of A. This number, 4, is the scale factor squared.

2. The surface area of C is none times the surface area of A. This number, 9, is the scale factor squared.

3. The surface are of Y is K^2 times the surface area of X.

Try This

1. 54 cm^2
2. 16 × 54 cm^2 = 864 cm^2

Hands-On Lab 10-5
Think and Discuss

1. Possible Answer: The two prisms are identical: one is rotated. It is an optical illusion that makes prism 2 seem larger.

Try This

1. The surface area is 62.80 cm^2

2. Possible Answer: It is more than double the surface area of cylinder 1 because the surface area if the circular bases varies as the square of the radius.

Hands-On Lab Recording Sheet 11-4
Activity 1
Think and Discuss

1. Possible Answer: The experimental probability based on combined results is closer to the theoretical probability than the experimental probability based on the results of an individual's experiment.

2. Possible Answer: 125

Try This

1. $\frac{1}{5}$, 0.2, 20%
2. Possible Answer: 100

Activity 2
Think and Discuss

1. The probability is $\frac{1}{12}$, because there are 4 × 3 possible outcomes

2. Possible answer: 50

3. The experimental probability is a summary of the results of repeated trials. The theoretical probability is a calculation based on the number of favorable outcomes and the total number of possible outcomes.

Try This

1. a. HH, HT, TH, TT
   b. Possible answer: 25
   c. Possible answer: 250

2. a. red-1, red-2, red-3, red-4, red-5, red-6, blue-1, blue-2, blue-3, blue-4, blue-5, blue-6, green-1, green-2, green-3, green-4, green-5, green-6
   b. Possible answer: Spin the spinner and roll the number cube 100 times. Keep track of the number of times the spinner lands on green and you roll a 6. Divide this number by the number of trials(100).

Hands-On Lab 11-4
Activity

Answers will vary based on experimental results. Possible answer: 1, 3, 2, 5, 1, 6, 4, 2, 3, 1, 4, 5, 6, 6, 1, 2, 5, 4, 5, 1, 3, 3, 4, 1, 6, 5, 6, 2, 3, 2

Possible answer: $6\frac{6}{30}$, $\frac{1}{5}$

Possible answer: The results are different, but the experiment is close to the theoretical as expected.

Holt Mathematics

Answer Key

Think and Discuss

1. Possible answer: You would expect 5 ones. Then the experimental probability would be $\frac{5}{30}$, or $\frac{1}{6}$, which is the same as the theoretical probability.

2. Possible answer: The theoretical probability tells what is expected on one trial. But since every outcome has some chance on every trial, it is unlikely that the results will exactly match what is expected over a number of trials.

Try This

1. Answers will vary based on experimental results. Answers below relating to experimental probability will use these numbers: 1, 3, 4, 2, 4, 5, 6, 6, 3, 2, 5, 1, 5, 3, 5, 4, 1, 6 ,5, 6, 2, 4, 1, 4, 3, 6, 5, 6, 1, 3

2. Theoretical Probability $\frac{1}{6}$ $\frac{1}{2}$ $\frac{1}{3}$

   Experimental Probability $\frac{1}{5}$ $\frac{7}{15}$ $\frac{4}{15}$

3. Possible Answer: The experimental probability of getting a 6 was higher than the theoretical. The experimental probability of getting an even number was slightly lower than the theoretical. The experimental probability of getting a number less than 3 is slightly less than the theoretical.

Hands-On Lab 11-5
Activity

1, $\frac{5}{9}$

2. There will be 5 light balls since the number does not change.

   There will be 9 balls since the number of balls has remained the same.

   The probability of selecting a light ball again is $\frac{5}{9}$.

3. There will be 4 light balls, since one has been removed. Since one is gone, there will be 8 balls left. The probability of selecting a light ball will be $\frac{4}{8}$ or $\frac{1}{2}$.

Think and Discuss

1. "With replacement" means you take something then return it so that the objects in the bag remain the same. "Without replacement" means you take something out o the bag and keep it out, so that the number of objects in the bag is reduced.

2. Since the object is not replaced, the composition of the group is changed which affects all following probabilities.

Try This

1. $\frac{2}{15}$

2. $\frac{1}{3}$

3. $\frac{4}{15}$

Hands-On Lab 11-6
Think and Discuss

1. Possible answer: The order is not important because the purpose of the combination is simply to determine who is on the team.

2. Answer Row 7: 1, 7, 21, 35, 35, 21, 7, 1
   Answer Row 8: 1, 8, 28, 56, 70, 56, 28, 8, 1

3. Possible answer: Every row starts and ends with 1. Every number in a row is the sum of the two numbers on either side of it and above it.

4. Possible Answer: The answer is always 1. If the number of items in each combination is equal to the total number of items, there is only one possible combination.

5. look at row 10 column 5: 252

Hands-On Lab 11-7
Think and Discuss

1. Yes

2. Yes

3. all the big marbles; all the glass marbles

Try This

1. 0, 1, 2, 3, 4, 5, 6, 7, 8, 9, 10

2. 5, 6, 7

Holt Mathematics

Answer Key

Activity

2.

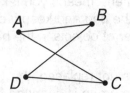

Think and Discuss

1. Sample answer: No. The path A to C to B to A is the reverse of the path A to B to C to A.

2. Sample answer: No. For example, the path from A to B to C to D to A would become the path from B to C to D to A to B.

3. Sample answer: No: The only choices are A to B to C to D to A; A to B to D to C to A; A to C to B to D to A. The choice A to C to D to B to A is the reverse of the path A to B to D to C to A.

Try This

1.

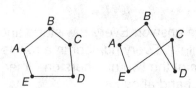

2. 6 paths

3.

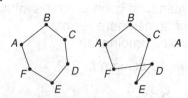

Hands-On Lab Recording Sheet 12-1
Think and Discuss

1. The Addition property of Equality states that you must add the same number to both sides of the equation for the statement to remain here.

2. Together, six yellow and six red unit tiles are equivalent to 0.

3. To model $3x - 5 = 10$, use 3 yellow

variable tiles and 5 red tiles on the left side. Use the 10 yellow unit tiles on the right side. In order to remove 5 red tiles from the left side, you have to add 0 (5 yellow unit tiles and 5 red unit tiles) to the right side. After removing 5 red tiles from each side, you are left with the equation $3x = 15$. Separate the 15 yellow unit tiles on the right into 3 equal groups to solve for the variable. You find that $x = 5$.

4. Use the model for $3n + 6 = -15$, but substitute 7 red tiles for each yellow variable tile. Then check to see that both sides of the equation are equal.

Try This

1. $x = 8$

2. $r = -5$

3. $m = 7$

4. $n = -11$

5. $j = 7$

6. $r = 2$

7. $h = 2$

8. $g = -3$

9. $k = 4$

Hands-On Lab 12-3
Think and Discuss

1. Subtract 5 from each side of the equation, then divide both sides by 4.

2. Adding negative tiles.

3. Subtract the variable from both sides of the equation.

4. Subtract the variable x from each side of the equation.

5. division

Try This

1. $x = 9$

2. $x = -13$

3. $x = -1$

4. $x = -3$

5. $x = 4$

6. $x = -6$

Holt Mathematics

Answer Key

7. $x = -5$

8. $x = 1$

Hands-On Lab 12-6
Activity

1. a. $x < 5$
   b. $x < 6$
   c. $x > 6$
   d. $x > -2$
2. a. $x < 8$
   b. $x < 12$
   c. $x > 2$
   e. $x > 2$
3. a. $x < 1$
   b. $x < 3$
   c. $x > -3$
   d. $x > 2$

Think and Discuss

1. Inequalities have a range of possible solutions.
2. $a < c$
3. no
4. Add 9 to both sides.
5. Subtract 5 from both sides; divide both sides by 4.

Try This

1. $x > 10$
2. $x < 4$
3. $x > 3$
4. $x > 5$
5. $x > 9$
6. $x < 8$
7. $x > 6$
8. $x < 2$

Holt Mathematics